VOL **2** AQU-BIO
87–174

FUNK & WAGNALLS **new**
# ENCYCLOPEDIA OF SCIENCE

FUNK & WAGNALLS, INC.

# HOW TO USE FUNK & WAGNALLS NEW ENCYCLOPEDIA OF SCIENCE

Volumes 1 through 21 have information printed on the front covers, spine, and title pages that make it easy to find the articles you want to read.

- Volume numbers are printed in all three places in Volumes 1 through 21.
- Letter breaks — $\frac{COL}{DIA}$ — are printed in all three places in Volumes 1 through 21. The letters above the line are the first three letters of the first article title in the volume. The letters below the line are the first three letters of the last article title in the volume.
- Page breaks — $\frac{351}{438}$ — are printed on the spines and title pages of Volumes 1 through 21. They provide the page numbers of the first and last text pages in the volume.

Articles are arranged alphabetically by title in Volumes 1 through 21. Most titles are printed in **BOLD-FACE CAPITAL** letters. Some titles are printed in even larger letters.

- Some titles are not article titles, but refer you to the actual article title. Within articles you will find *See* or *See also* other article names for further information. All of these references to other articles are called cross-references.
- Most article titles are followed by a phonetic pronunciation. Use the Pronunciation Guide on page vi of Volume 1 to learn the correct pronunciation of the article title.
- At the end of most articles are two sets of initials. The first set identifies the person who wrote the article. The second set identifies the special consultant who checked the article for accuracy. All of these people are listed by their initials and full names and position on pages v and vi of Volume 1.
- ◣ This symbol at the end of an article indicates that there is a project based on the subject of the article in the Projects, Bibliography & Index volume. The project is found under its article title, and all of the project article titles are arranged alphabetically on pages 1 through 64 of the Projects, Bibliography & Index volume.

The Projects, Bibliography & Index Volume contains three sections. Each is an essential part of the encyclopedia.

- Projects based on articles in the encyclopedia are found in the first section. Each is both entertaining and educational. Each is designed for use by a student and for parental participation if desired.
- Bibliography reading lists in the second section list books under general scientific categories that are also titles of major articles. Each book listed is marked with either a YA (Young Adult) or J (Juvenile) reading level indicator. YA generally applies to readers at the junior high level or higher. J applies to readers at grade levels below junior high school.
- Index entries for all article titles plus many subjects that are not article titles are found in the third section. Instructions on using the Index are found at the start of the Index section in the Projects, Bibliography & Index volume.

**AQUARIUS** (ə kwar′ ē əs) Aquarius is the name of one of the 12 constellations of the zodiac. These constellations lie in a circle around the sun. As the earth follows its orbit, people see different constellations. The stars of the Aquarius constellation are not very bright. They can usually be seen during the month of September in the southern sky. The Aquarius constellation is between the constellations of Capricorn and Pisces. (*See* ZODIAC.)

Aquarius is sometimes called the Water Bearer or the Water Boy. The stars of Aquarius form the end points of a Y shape. The top of the Y looks like a jug or pail of water. The bottom line of the Y is seen as a stream of water from the jug.    G.M.B./C.R.

**AQUATIC PLANT** (ə kwät′ ik plant) An aquatic plant is a plant that lives in water. It is also called a hydrophyte, which means "water plant." There are many different forms of aquatic plants. They may belong to many different plant divisions. (*See* PLANT KINGDOM.) Submerged plants are species that live completely under water. Most of the algae are examples of this form. Floating plants float freely on the surface of the water. Duckweed and wolffia are floating plants. Emergent plants have their roots and bases in the water, but grow leaves above the water surface. A cattail plant is a tall, emergent plant.

Plants that live in the water must adapt to conditions that do not exist on land. Submerged leaves and stems of aquatic plants do not have a thick, waxy cuticle to prevent evaporation as land plants do. (*See* LEAF.) Many submerged plants do not have roots. They must absorb water and minerals through the leaf surface. Some algae that are exposed to the air at low tide are covered with mucus to prevent their drying out.

The pollen of flowering plants on land is spread by wind and insects. (*See* POLLINATION.) This cannot occur with submerged flowering plants. These species have de- veloped methods of underwater pollination.

Aquatic plants are important members of the water environment. They supply food, shelter, and oxygen for many animals. If aquatic plants grow too plentiful, they can clog waterways and cause other problems. This growth is usually the result of water pollution.    S.R.G./M.H.S.

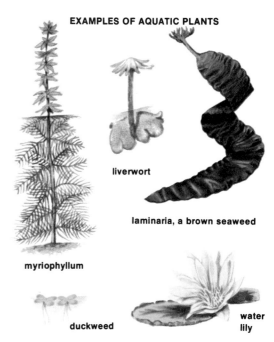

**EXAMPLES OF AQUATIC PLANTS**

liverwort

laminaria, a brown seaweed

myriophyllum

duckweed

water lily

Aquatic plants are found all over the world. They grow in both freshwater and marine environments. All life in the sea depends on its plants.

**AQUEDUCT** (ak′ wə dəkt′) An aqueduct is a structure or artificial channel that carries water from one place to another. It can consist of a pipeline above or below the ground, a tunnel, or an open ditch. It may also be a bridgelike structure that carries water across a valley. Water moves through an aqueduct either by means of gravity or under pressure from pumps. Aqueducts are used to bring drinking water to cities and irrigation water to farm lands. They are also used in hydroelectric projects. (*See* HYDROELECTRIC POWER.)

The aqueducts that are used to bring drinking water to cities can be hundreds of miles long. The Colorado River Aqueduct uses a combination of concrete-lined tunnels and open canals to carry water 389 km [242 mi] to Los Angeles. The longest aqueduct in the world is the California Aqueduct. It also serves the city of Los Angeles and is 715 km [444 mi] long.

The Romans built large aqueducts in Europe two thousand years ago. The remains of many of these are still standing. The Pont Du Gard aqueduct at Nîmes, France, and another at Segovia, Spain, are the best known. *See also* IRRIGATION; WATER SUPPLY.

W.R.P./R.W.L.

**AQUILA** (ak′ wə lə) Aquila is the name of a constellation of stars in the northern hemisphere. It is a part of the Milky Way. It can usually be seen during the summer in the southern sky. The Aquila constellation includes Altair, which is one of the 15 brightest stars in the sky. Altair is sometimes called alpha Aquilae. It is bigger than our sun and gives out more light. Altair is about 16 light-years distant from earth. The Aquila constellation is also called the Eagle.    G.M.B./C.R.

**ARACHNID** (ə rak′ nəd) Arachnids are a class of animals in the group of joint-legged creatures called Arthropoda. The arachnids include spiders, harvestmen, ticks, mites, and scorpions. They have four pairs of legs, two-part bodies, no antennae, and no wings. They also have two small fangs at the front of their heads. Arachnids do not eat solid food. They extract juices from animals and plants.

Arachnids are sometimes mistaken for insects. There are several differences between insects and arachnids. Arachnids have two more legs than insects. Insects, unlike arachnids, have antennae and often have wings. *See also* HARVESTMAN; PARASITE.

G.M.B./J.R.

**ARBORETUM** (är′ bə rēt′ əm) An arboretum is a garden where woody plants such

Various kinds of arachnids: 1. scorpion, with sting poised; 2. a blood-sucking tick; 3. one kind of spider; 4. a ricinuleid; 5. the stingless whip scorpion; 6. a pseudoscorpion, or false scorpion, which cannot sting; 7. harvestman, or daddy longlegs; 8. a solifuge. All arachnids have eight legs. This distinguishes them from insects, which have just six legs.

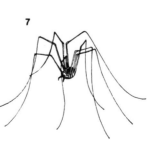

as trees and shrubs are grown for decorative, educational, or scientific purposes. The first arboretum was founded in France during the mid-1500s. Some of the best-known arboretums in the United States are Brooklyn Botanical Garden (Brooklyn, New York), National Arboretum (Washington, D.C.), and Morton Arboretum (Lisle, Illinois).

S.R.G./M.H.S.

**ARBORVITAE** (är′ bər vīt′ ē) Arborvitae is a common name for a group of evergreen trees that belongs to the genus *Thuja*. Arborvitae means "tree of life" in Latin. Early explorers of North America gave the trees this name. When the explorers were visiting the area now known as Canada, they suffered from the disease scurvy. The native Indians made a tea from the arborvitae tree. This tea helped restore the explorers' health. *See also* CEDAR.

S.R.G./M.H.S.

**ARC, ELECTRIC** An electric arc (ärk) is one of the ways in which electricity can flow through a gas. Electric arcs can be formed by putting a very high voltage across two electrodes. The electrodes are usually metal or carbon. The electric arc is a stream of electrons and ions passing between the electrodes. The arc gives out a bright light because electrons hit gas molecules between the electrodes. This causes the molecules to give off light.

The light from electric arcs is very bright. Arc lights give a very white light from an arc between two carbon electrodes. Arc lights were once used in television and film studios, and in searchlights.

When an electric arc passes between two electrodes, the electrodes become very hot. Arc furnaces use arcs to melt steel and other metals. Arc welding uses an electric arc to melt and join metals.

M.E./J.T.

**ARCHAEOPTERYX** (är′ kē äp′ tə riks) The archaeopteryx is the earliest known bird.

The word archaeopteryx means "ancient one with wings." The archaeopteryx evolved from reptiles and lived during the time of the dinosaurs, about 150 million years ago. The first fossil remains of an archaeopteryx were found in Germany in the 1800s.

The archaeopteryx was about 50.8 cm [20 in] long. It did not fly very well, probably only short distances. Its wing muscles were not very large. Unlike the pterodactyl, or flying reptile, the archaeopteryx flapped its wings. The pterodactyl was a glider. It did not flap its wings.

The skeleton of an archaeopteryx is like the skeleton of a reptile. Unlike reptiles, which had scales, the archaeopteryx had feathers. Three clawed "fingers" were at the ends of each of its two wing bones. It used its fingers and feet for climbing. The beak of an archaeopteryx contained teeth. Its long tail had 20 vertebrae and a pair of feathers.

G.M.B./L.L.S.

The archaeopteryx is the earliest birdlike creature we know about. Scientists believe that this animal evolved from a reptile.

**ARCHEGONIUM** (är′ ki gō′ nē əm) The archegonium is the female sex organ in lower plants such as ferns and mosses. It is bottle-shaped with a long, thin neck. In the base of the archegonium is the egg. The male sex organ, the antheridium, produces a sperm which enters the neck of the archegonium. The sperm travels down into the base where it joins with the egg. The fertilized egg is called a zygote. The zygote will become a new plant which will disperse itself either by developing seeds or spores.

A.J.C./M.H.S.

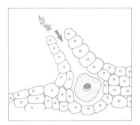

The archegonium, or female sex organ, of a fern. A sperm is shown entering the neck to fertilize the egg within. The fertilized egg will grow into a fern. The archegonium is on the prothallus.

**ARCHEOLOGY** (är′ kē äl′ ə jē) Archeology is the scientific study of the physical traces of people of the past. It deals with objects made by people and with the remains of people, plants, and animals. These objects and remains often must be dug up from beneath the earth or water. The purpose of archeology is to explain what people were like in the past and how they lived.

Persons who work in archeology are called archeologists. They often have been trained in other sciences like anthropology, biology, geology, and zoology. They use picks and shovels as well as microscopes and radioactive testing in their work.

The first thing an archeologist must do is search for the places where people of the past have lived. The archeologist is like a detective who must solve a mystery. He or she searches for camps, houses, villages, and cities that might be buried. An archeologist also explores caves and underground cemeteries called tombs.

The things that archeologists find become pieces of a puzzle. They tell a story of the past. All of the puzzle's pieces cannot always be found. Stone and metal objects may be found. The bones of humans and animals are sometimes found. Fossils are often found. Some things, however, are lost to decomposition. Items made of straw, cloth, or wood are rarely found. Burned wood in the form of charcoal is very valuable to an archeologist. It is wood that has not decomposed, permitting an archeologist to decide the time that has gone by since its origin.

Archeologists working in places where the climate is dry, like Egypt and coastal Peru, and also in very wet places like bogs, find things that are well preserved. In places where the climate changes, physical traces of man are not usually well preserved.

Archeologists carefully study the objects they find. They also make very careful records of where these objects were found and what they look like. Archeologists use these studies to establish information about people who lived hundreds or thousands of years ago. Carvings on pots tell the archeologist about the kind of art people produced. The construction of their houses tells about their building skills. The bones of animals might tell what kind of food they ate. Weapons and tools tell about their intelligence.

Archeology is divided into categories of time and location. Archeologists who study ancient Egypt are also called Egyptologists. Other archeologists might study medieval archeology or industrial archeology.

Archeology began in the 1500s when the people of Europe became interested in the ancient civilizations of Rome, Greece, and Egypt. Thomas Jefferson of the United States studied Indian mounds in Virginia in 1784. His archeology is considered the first to be done in the modern or scientific way. Archeology before that was mainly a hunt for things to sell to museums and collectors. Unscientific archeology of this sort was like a child's treasure hunt. It destroyed things that modern archeologists would have saved. Archeologists today are going back over some of the diggings of earlier archeologists to check for mistakes. Since the 1930s, archeology has become a precise science with strict rules and procedures.

Some of the most famous finds of archeology are the Rosetta Stone of Egypt and the Dead Sea Scrolls of Israel. The Rosetta Stone was found in 1799. It was the chief clue to understanding hieroglyphics, which are the symbols of the written language of ancient Egypt. The Dead Sea Scrolls were found in 1947. They are the first known writings of the Bible. In the United States, archeologists are often called to places where construction workers uncover signs of old Indian life. In Central and South America, archeologists have uncovered the ruins of great Indian civilizations. Collecting arrowheads is a form of archeology that is often the hobby of American children.

Modern technology has advanced archeology. Scientists today are able to determine the age of archeological objects by using chemistry and electronics. Some prehistoric objects are tested for radiocarbon, potassium, and argon content. Instruments for measuring these contents can sometimes tell archeologists how many thousands or millions of years the object has been in its present form. *See also* FOSSIL; PREHISTORY.

G.M.B./S.O.

**ARCHEOZOIC ERA** (är′ kē ə zō′ ik ir′ ə) The Archeozoic era is the period in the earth's history to which the oldest rocks and the earliest known forms of life belong. It followed the Azoic era, which started when the earth was formed. The Archeozic era ended about 1,850 million years ago, when the Proterozoic era began. Lava rocks from the Archeozoic era, dating from one to two billion years ago, are found all over the world.

During the Archeozoic era, the oldest mountains in North America, the Laurentians in Canada, were formed. Radioactive dating has shown rocks of the Archeozoic era to be at the base of the Adirondacks, the Colorado Rocky Mountains, and in the Grand Canyon.

There are two main kinds of rocks from this period: the upper sedimentary Timiskaming rocks, which have settled to the bottoms of various bodies of water, and the lower, or keewatin, greenstone rocks. The lower rocks have a strange "pillow shape," caused by lava dropping into water. These rocks have changed so much that their original makeup is unknown. Granites, gneisses, and schists are found in this group. The search for Archaean rock, the oldest rock known to date, has increased greatly because the rock often contains gold and silver.

The first known signs of life on earth, the algae, were found fossilized in the Archeozoic rocks in Swaziland, Africa. These fossils are believed to be around 3,500 million years old.                           J.J.A./W.R.S.

**ARCHERFISH** (är′ chər fish′) An archerfish is a freshwater fish that belongs to the family Toxotidae. It is found in India and Indonesia. It gets its name from the way it captures food. The archerfish has an elongated snout through which it can squirt water. When the fish sees an insect sitting on a leaf above the water, it squirts water at it. The water knocks the insect into the water. The archerfish then eats the fallen insect. The fish can aim the stream of water remarkably well.

S.R.G./E.C.M.

The archerfish shoots down its prey with a jet of water. When the prey falls into the water, the fish eats it.

**ARCHIMEDES** (about 287–212 B.C.) (är′ kə mēd′ ēz) Archimedes, called the "father of experimental science," was an ancient Greek physicist, mathematician, and inventor. Among other things, Archimedes discovered how to use levers and pulleys to lift heavy objects, such as large ships. He also learned how to pump water uphill by using his invention, the Archimedean screw. In mathematics, he found out how to measure the area of circles and other figures. He worked out a value for pi ($\pi$) and came close to inventing calculus.

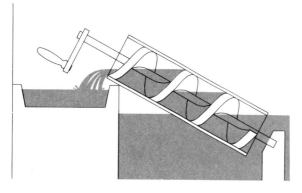

This is a diagram of the Archimedian screw. This simple but effective machine raises water when the handle is turned. This system is still used to irrigate fields in many parts of the world.
This machine is said to be the best known of the inventions of Archimedes.

Archimedes spent most of his life in Syracuse, a city of Sicily, which is an island near Italy. Here he derived the famous Archimedes' principle, which states that when a solid object is immersed in a liquid, it is pushed up in the liquid by a force equal to the weight of the liquid that has been displaced by the object. It is said that Archimedes discovered this principle in a strange way. According to the story, the king of Syracuse asked Archimedes to tell him if his new crown was pure gold. Archimedes thought of a way to test the crown. He had noticed that when he stepped into a full bathtub, the tub overflowed. His body had displaced a certain amount of water. He concluded that a crown of pure gold should displace the same amount of water as a chunk of pure gold weighing the same as the crown. When making the test, he discovered that the crown was not pure gold. The goldsmith had cheated the king.

Archimedes designed war machines for his king. It is said that he invented giant mirrors to focus the sun's rays in order to burn enemy ships attacking Syracuse. Archimedes' genius helped the king hold off his enemies for three years. Archimedes is said to have been killed during the final battle for the city, when the Romans took over Syracuse. *See also* RELATIVE DENSITY.   J.J.A./D.G.F.

**ARGO** (är' gō) Argo is the old name of a constellation of stars in the southern hemisphere of the sky. It was given its name by Ptolemy, who was an astronomer of ancient Greece. He named the constellation after a ship in the legend of Jason and the Argonauts. Modern astronomers have divided the Argo constellation into the four constellations Vela, Puppis, Carina, and Pyxis.

The Argo constellation is best seen in the month of December. It is a part of the Milky Way. The Argo constellation includes Canopus, which is the second brightest star in the southern sky. Four of the stars in the Argo constellation are sometimes mistaken for another constellation called the Southern Cross. Because of this, these four stars are called the False Cross constellation.

G.M.B./C.R.

**ARGON** (är' gän') Argon is a colorless, odorless gaseous element. Its symbol is Ar. It has an atomic number of 18 and an atomic weight of 39.95. It boils at $-186°C$ [$-303°F$] and melts at $-189°C$ [$-308°F$]. It was discovered in 1894 by the British scientists Sir William Ramsay and Lord Rayleigh.

One percent of the air is argon. Argon can be obtained from the air by separating it from the other gases. This is done by liquifying the air. The argon is then separated by distillation. Argon is one of the noble gases. (*See* NOBLE GAS.) This means that it is chemically inactive. It does not combine easily with other elements. Because of this, it is used in electric light bulbs. A more reactive gas would attack the hot filament.   M.E./J.R.W.

**ARIES** (ar′ ē ēz′) Aries is the name of one of the 12 constellations in the zodiac. It is a constellation of the northern hemisphere. The three brightest stars of the Aries constellation are Hamal, Sheratan, and Mesartim. These stars form the points of an imaginary ram's head. The ram's body is outlined by stars that often are difficult to see. *See also* ZODIAC.

G.M.B./C.R.

**ARISTOTLE (384–322 B.C.)** Aristotle (ar′ is tŏt′ əl) was a Greek philosopher and scientist who developed many ideas about the nature of life and matter. He also wrote on literature, politics, and ethics. He introduced logic, or systematic reasoning, into science. This was important because it allowed scientists to verify, or test the truth of, their ideas by observation. Aristotle did much work in biology and zoology. He was the first person to classify animals on the basis of structure and behavior. Aristotle stated that dolphins are mammals, not fish. This idea was not believed for hundreds of years, until proven in the 1800s. He also put forward some of the first ideas on human evolution.

Aristotle's theories were widely believed in the Middle Ages. Some of his ideas may have kept science from moving forward during that period. For instance, Aristotle mistakenly thought that heavy objects fall faster than light objects. He also believed that the sun revolved around the earth. In the 1500s and 1600s, men like Newton, Galileo, and Copernicus proved these ideas wrong.

W.R.P./D.G.F.

**Aristotle**

# ARITHMETIC

Arithmetic (ə rith′ mə tik′) is the study of the addition, subtraction, multiplication, and division of numbers. It is the oldest and simplest branch of mathematics. Cave people who counted on their fingers were doing arithmetic. They could see that their hands had five fingers each, and each foot had five toes.

It is easy to see if two groups of objects have the same number of features. Match each object in the first group with one from the second. A group of five sheep, the fingers on one hand, and a pile of five marbles all have something in common, which is the number five.

The number of fingers was probably the basis of arithmetic. That is why number systems often use groups of fives or tens. A simple way of recording numbers may be by using marbles. This becomes a problem, however, when dealing in large numbers. A better way is to use symbols in place of objects.

The Roman system was very simple, using only a few symbols. For example, 15 would be written as ten (X) with five (V), or XV. 378 would be written as CCCLXXVIII. However, it was very complicated to multiply and divide using Roman numerals.

| Roman numerals | I | V | X | L | C | D | M |
|---|---|---|---|---|---|---|---|
| Value | 1 | 5 | 10 | 50 | 100 | 500 | 1000 |

The number system we now use comes from the Hindu-Arabic numerals. This system uses the symbols, 1, 2, 3, 4, 5, 6, 7, 8, 9, 0. Using these ten numerals, it is possible to write any number by combining the symbols in different ways. The position of the symbol tells whether it is of units, tens, hundreds and so on. For example, in the number 238, the 8 stands for eight units, the 3 for three tens, and the 2 for two hundreds. A symbol for zero is necessary in order to tell the differences among twenty-three (23), two hundred three (203), and two hundred thirty (230).

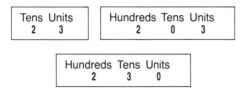

Two groups of things can be combined to make a larger group. When this is done, it is called addition, the basis of arithmetic. Adding can be done by counting the amount of the first number, and then counting on from the first number an amount equal to the second number.

Our system groups numbers in tens. It is possible to add the units together, and then the tens, the hundreds, and so on. The diagram shows what happens when 26 and 38 are added together. The 6 and 8 give a total of 14, or a group of ten, and four units.

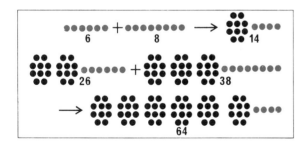

This means a total of six groups of ten altogether, with four more units, written as 64.

The reverse of addition is subtraction. To subtract one number from another, a person may think in terms of addition. For example,

the problem, "What is 8 when 5 is taken away from it?" may be thought of as, "What number added to 5 gets 8?" The statement 8 − 5 = 3 is true if 3 + 5 = 8. Subtraction may be thought of in terms of the general question, "What must be added to the smaller number to get to the larger number?" The largest number is called the minuend. The number after it is the subtrahend, and the answer is the difference. Adding the subtrahend and the difference equals the minuend if the answer is correct.

To multiply two numbers together is to carry out a process of repeated addition. 5 × 4 means four lots of 5 added together, or 5 + 5 + 5 + 5. This problem may also be seen as five lots of 4 added together, or 4 + 4 + 4 + 4 + 4. Tables for multiplication can be worked out by repeated addition. An easy way to set out the tables is in the form of a square.

| X | 1 | 2 | 3 | 4 | 5 | 6 | 7 | 8 | 9 |
|---|---|---|---|---|---|---|---|---|---|
| 1 | 1 | 2 | 3 | 4 | 5 | 6 | 7 | 8 | 9 |
| 2 | 2 | 4 | 6 | 8 | 10 | 12 | 14 | 16 | 18 |
| 3 | 3 | 6 | 9 | 12 | 15 | 18 | 21 | 24 | 27 |
| 4 | 4 | 8 | 12 | 16 | 20 | 24 | 28 | 32 | 36 |
| 5 | 5 | 10 | 15 | 20 | 25 | 30 | 35 | 40 | 45 |
| 6 | 6 | 12 | 18 | 24 | 30 | 36 | 42 | 48 | 54 |
| 7 | 7 | 14 | 21 | 28 | 35 | 42 | 49 | 56 | 63 |
| 8 | 8 | 16 | 24 | 32 | 40 | 48 | 56 | 64 | 72 |
| 9 | 9 | 18 | 27 | 36 | 45 | 54 | 63 | 72 | 81 |

Multiplying by 10 shifts each digit over one place to the left. The units become tens, the tens become hundreds, and so on.

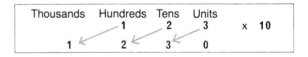

To multiply by a number like 37, multiply by 7 and by 30 and add the two results together. Multiplying by 30 is to multiply by 3 and shift the result one place to the left. 123 in this case is the multiplicand, 37 the multiplier, and 4551 the product.

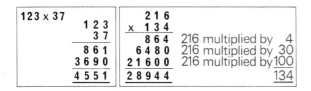

Square numbers are numbers produced by taking any number and multiplying that number by itself. Square numbers can be shown as sets of dots arranged in squares. An interesting pattern appears in going from one square number to the next.

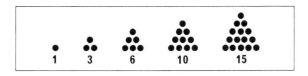

The triangular numbers are 1, 3, 6, 10 . . . It is easy to spot the pattern formed by moving from one triangular number to the next.

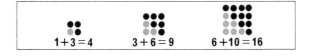

The diagram shows an interesting connection between the triangular numbers and the square numbers.

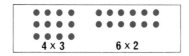

Rectangular numbers can be arranged as a number of equal rows. 12 can be shown as 3 rows of 4 or 2 rows of 6.

Some numbers can be shown only as a single row of dots. These numbers have only 1 and themselves as factors. Whenever a number divides evenly into another number, it is called a factor.

The fourth operation of arithmetic is division. "What is 24 divided by 6?" may be thought of in terms of multiplication, or "What number multiplied by 6 gets 24?" In the statement, "24 divided by 6 equals 4," 6 is the divisor, 4 is the quotient, and 24 is the dividend.

The numbers used in this discussion of arithmetic were all whole numbers, called integers. There are many other kinds of numbers, such as fractions. For example, a cake can be cut into four equal pieces. Each piece is a fraction, or part of, the whole cake. Each piece is one-fourth, written as ¼, of the whole cake.

Using decimal numbers is a quick way to write fractions. Decimal numbers are used because they are easy to multiply and divide. The fraction ¼ is written as .25 when written as a decimal number. The period in a decimal number is called a decimal point.

Mathematicians took centuries to develop the methods now used in arithmetic. Everyone who goes to school learns arithmetic. It is a skill necessary in science, business, and everyday life. Exploring numbers and their various uses can, in itself, be a fascinating study.                    J.J.A./S.P.A.

**ARMADILLO** (är′ mə dil′ ō) An armadillo is a mammal belonging to the order Edentata. It has a tough, hard covering that looks like plates of armor. These plates are called scutes. There are 20 kinds of armadillos. They can be found from the southern United States to Argentina. Armadillos are pinkish or brown in color.

Armadillos eat insects, spiders, earthworms, and land snails. They have long tongues for licking up their food. They have small teeth at the backs of their mouths. Armadillos cannot bite. They use their strong claws to dig tunnels and burrows in the ground.

The fairy armadillo is about 15 cm [6 in] long. It is the smallest armadillo. The giant armadillo is about 1.5 m [5 ft] long. It is the largest armadillo. The nine-banded armadillo is about 60 cm [2 ft] long. It is the only kind of armadillo found in the United States. It lives chiefly in the most southern states, but scientists say it is moving northward. The nine-banded armadillo gets its name from the nine movable bands of armor on its body. All other kinds of armadillos have 3 to 18 movable armor bands on their bodies. The nine-banded armadillo weighs about 6.75 kg [15 lb]. The female of this species gives birth to four babies, which are always of the same sex.

Some armadillos are killed or trapped because they damage crops. They also damage the foundations of buildings with their underground tunnels and burrows. Some people eat the armadillo's meat. *See also* AARDVARK; ANTEATER; SLOTH.                    G.M.B./J.J.M.

Armadillos are small animals that have protective bony plates on their skin.

### ARMSTRONG, NEIL ALDEN (1930–

Neil Armstrong (ärm′ sträng), an American astronaut, was the first person to set foot on the moon. On July 20, 1969, he and Edwin "Buzz" Aldrin, Jr. landed the Apollo 11 lunar module on the moon. Armstrong was commander of the mission. He stepped onto the moon at 10:56 P.M., eastern daylight saving time. His words, radioed back to earth, were, "That's one small step for man, one giant leap for mankind."

Armstrong was born in Wapakoneta, Ohio. He received a degree in aeronautical engineering from Purdue University. He be-

came a test pilot and flew research airplanes for NASA (National Aeronautics and Space Administration). The rocket-powered X-15 was one of the planes he tested. Armstrong and David R. Scott were the crew of the Gemini 8 flight in March, 1966. The first space docking of two vehicles was made on this flight.

Armstrong resigned from NASA in 1971 and began teaching engineering at the University of Cincinnati. *See also* PROJECT APOLLO.
                    W.R.P./D.G.F.

Neil Armstrong, the American astronaut who in 1969 became the first person to walk on the moon. He did this during the Apollo 11 mission, of which he was commander.

### AROMATIC AND ALIPHATIC COMPOUNDS

Aromatic (ar′ ə mat′ ik) and aliphatic (al′ ə fat′ ik) compounds, are types of compounds in organic chemistry. Aliphatic compounds have molecules made of long chains of carbon atoms to which other atoms are attached. Normal-hexane ($CH_3CH_2CH_2CH_2CH_2CH_3$) is an aliphatic compound. Aromatic compounds are benzene and compounds made from benzene. Benzene ($C_6H_6$) is made of six CH groups arranged in a ring. Aromatic compounds are made from benzene by replacing one or more of the hydrogen atoms in the ring with other groups. One example is naphthalene. Compounds containing rings of carbon atoms not made from benzene are alicyclic compounds, such as cyclohexane. Cyclohexane is made of a ring of six $CH_2$ groups. Compounds containing rings of atoms which are not all carbon atoms are called heterocyclic compounds. *See also* HYDROCARBONS.                    J.J.A./J.M.

**ARRHENIUS, SVANTE** (1859–1927) Svante Arrhenius (ar rā′ ni əs) was a Swedish chemist and physicist who proposed that some substances gain or lose an electrical charge when they are dissolved in water. The substances are called electrolytes because their solutions conduct electricity. Arrhenius presented his theory in 1884. In 1903 he received the Nobel prize for chemistry. His work led to the discovery of the electron.

A.J.C./D.G.F.

**ARROW WORM** (ar′ ō wərm) An arrow worm is a small sea creature belonging to the phylum Chaetognatha. (*See* ANIMAL KINGDOM.) It ranges in length from 3 to 10 cm [1 to 4 in]. Most kinds are transparent. They are found in plankton. Arrow worms live at all depths in the ocean. 
S.R.G./C.S.H.

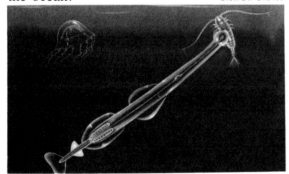
Arrow worms are transparent sea animals.

**ARSENIC** (ärs′ nik) Arsenic is an element with an atomic number of 33 and an atomic weight of 74.91. Its symbol is As. It has two different crystal forms called allotropes. One is a gray, metallic form; the other is yellow and nonmetallic. Gray arsenic does not melt. It goes straight from a solid to a gas. This is called sublimation. It sublimes at 613°C [1,135°F]. Its relative density is 5.7. Yellow arsenic is not stable. Its relative density is 1.97. Arsenic is found mainly in a dark red sulfide mineral called realgar and in another mineral called mispickel.

Most arsenic compounds are very poisonous. (*See* COMPOUND.) Paris green and lead arsenate are used as insecticides. Other arsenic compounds are used as weed killers and rat poisons. (*See* INSECTICIDE; POISON.) M.E./J.R.W.

**ARTERIOSCLEROSIS** (är tir′ ē ō sklə rō′ səs) Arteriosclerosis is a disease of the arteries, the blood vessels that carry blood from the heart to other parts of the body. The main symptom is a thickening and loss of elasticity in the arterial walls. The thickening makes the inside of the artery smaller, allowing less blood to flow through it. The disease is often called ''hardening of the arteries.''

There seems to be no single cause of arteriosclerosis. The disease has been found in people of all ages, though mostly in middle-aged and older people. The disease tends to develop in the body over a period of years.

The main form of arteriosclerosis is called atherosclerosis. Atherosclerosis results mainly from a build-up of fatty material in the artery walls. These plaques of fatty material, called atheromas, contain calcium, fatty acids, and cholesterol. Atheromas have rough edges that scrape the smooth walls of the arteries. Scar tissue forms. The arteries become hard and narrow, decreasing the flow of blood. Arteriolar sclerosis, another form of arteriosclerosis, is the hardening and thickening of the small arteries. Arteriolar sclerosis in the retina of the eye causes blurring of vision. If the blood pressure is not reduced, it will cause a wasting away, or atrophy, of the retina and optic nerve.

Arteriosclerosis can result in apoplexy or in a chest pain called angina pectoris. Physicians do not know how to prevent arteriosclerosis. Some believe the disease can be controlled by reducing the amount of cholesterol in a person's diet. People who have arteriosclerosis, especially atherosclerosis, are warned by doctors to stop smoking, to exercise every day, and to keep their weight within normal limits. In extreme cases, the diseased arteries can be removed and replaced with vessels from other parts of the body or with arteries made of synthetic materials such as Teflon and nylon. An alternative, less dangerous procedure is to insert a deflated balloon into the artery and inflate it when it reaches the diseased area. This acts to compress the fatty deposits and allows the blood flow to return to normal.

J.J.A./J.J.F.

**ARTERY** (ärt′ ə rē) An artery is a blood vessel shaped like a tube with thick, elastic, muscular walls. Arteries carry blood away from the heart and to the lungs. (See CIRCULATORY SYSTEM.) The main artery leaving the heart is the aorta. It carries bright red, oxygen-rich blood. The pulmonary artery carries blood containing too little oxygen to the lungs. As the heart pumps, a wave of pressure travels along the walls of the arteries and can be felt as a pulse. The smallest arteries are the arterioles. Their walls contract and relax and can regulate the amount of blood flowing to the body tissues. P.G.C./J.J.F.

**ARTESIAN WELL** (är tē′ zhən wel) An artesian well is a hole drilled or dug down to underground water. In an artesian well the water is trapped under great pressure between layers of rock. When the well is drilled, the pressure forces the water up through the hole.

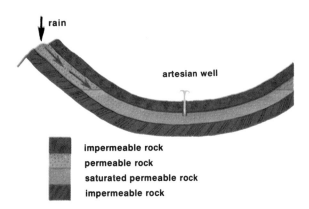

impermeable rock
permeable rock
saturated permeable rock
impermeable rock

In artesian wells, water is forced to the surface by pressure. The pressure results from the fact that the well is far below the level of the source of the water.

Water can be trapped underground between layers of solid rock called an aquifer. Sometimes a natural opening allows water from an aquifer to stream out of the ground. This is called an artesian spring.

Some surface water of the Rocky Mountains in the United States seeps underground to an aquifer that is called the Dakota sandstone. This aquifer is part of a large geological formation called an artesian basin. Many artesian wells and artesian springs are usually found in an artesian basin. The largest artesian basin in the world is the Great Australian Basin in Australia. *See also* GEOLOGY; GROUND WATER; WATER SUPPLY.

G.M.B./W.R.S.

**ARTHRITIS** (är thrīt′ əs) Arthritis is a name for a group of diseases that cause joints in the body to be painful. The name arthritis comes from the Greek meaning joint inflammation.

The term rheumatism is sometimes used for types of arthritis. Rheumatism is a general term. It refers to the inflamation of muscles, joints, and the parts of the body that connect them. Both arthritis and rheumatism are rheumatic diseases—diseases that attack and irritate the connecting tissues of the body. The connective tissues are those tissues which hold the body together, such as bone, cartilage, ligament, muscle, and tendon.

Arthritis can be a minor annoyance, or it can severely cripple a person. Arthritic joints may become very swollen and crooked. Sometimes these joints cannot be moved. Although arthritis is more common in older people, it can occur to people of any age. The disease attacks twice as many women as it does men. It is not restricted to humans. The dinosaurs of the Mesozoic era suffered from arthritis.

The exact cause of most kinds of arthritis is not known. Some types are caused by injuries or by high amounts of chemicals in the blood. Some types are caused by the wearing away of cartilage over a long life or by an allergenic reaction to medicine. (*See* AL-LERGY.) Some types of arthritis are thought to be caused by bacteria or viruses.

Scientists have recently discovered a type of arthritis that they believe is caused by a virus. It is spread to humans by a bite from a tick. The disease occurs only in three small towns in Connecticut and has been named Lyme Arthritis after the town of its origin—Lyme, Connecticut.

Arthritis is usually treated by aspirin-type drugs to reduce pain and swelling. Some people who suffer from arthritis are helped by physical therapy, which includes vigorous

body rubs and sound waves transmitted into the body. S.R.G./J.J.F.

**ARTHROPODA** (är thräp′ ə də) Arthropoda is the largest phylum of the animal kingdom. It contains about 80% of all the known species in the world. Insects, spiders, and crabs all belong to Arthropoda.

All arthropods have jointed legs. (*See* JOINT.) Arthropoda comes from the Greek words meaning jointed foot. Arthropods also have segmented bodies. Most species have a head, thorax, and abdomen. Arthropods do not have bones, but they do have a skeleton on

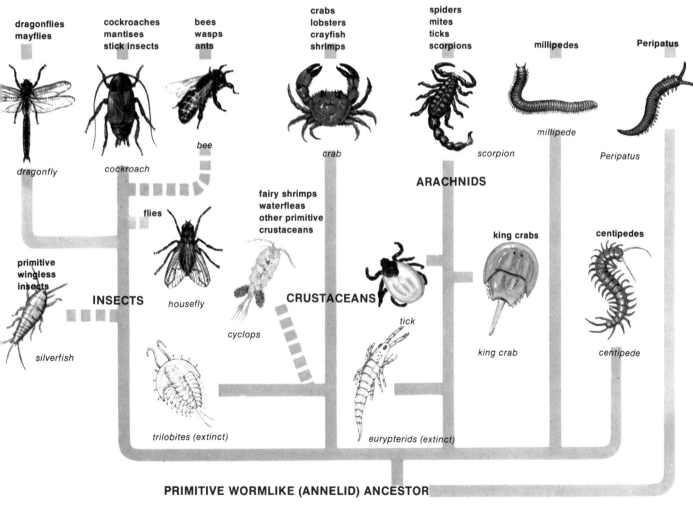

**dragonflies mayflies** — *dragonfly*

**cockroaches mantises stick insects** — *cockroach*

**bees wasps ants** — *bee*

**crabs lobsters crayfish shrimps** — *crab*

**spiders mites ticks scorpions** — *scorpion*

**millipedes** — *millipede*

**Peripatus** — *Peripatus*

**ARACHNIDS**

**fairy shrimps waterfleas other primitive crustaceans**

**flies** — *housefly*

**primitive wingless insects** — *silverfish*

**INSECTS**

*cyclops*

**CRUSTACEANS**

*tick*

**king crabs** — *king crab*

**centipedes** — *centipede*

*trilobites (extinct)*

*eurypterids (extinct)*

**PRIMITIVE WORMLIKE (ANNELID) ANCESTOR**

Arthropods, or joint-legged animals, are very widespread and varied in structure. This "family tree" presents the main groups of arthropods. Two extinct forms, the trilobites and the eurypterids lived more than 400 million years ago. A living fossil arthropod is the king crab, which is not a crab but an arachnid. The king crab has lived in the seas almost unchanged for 160 million years. The Peripatus is of special interest because it resembles the annelid worms, from which it evolved.

the outside of their bodies. This is called an exoskeleton. It is made up of a hard material called chitin. The covering of a lobster or a cricket is an example of a chitin exoskeleton. The exoskeleton is also called the cuticle.

Because the exoskeleton is hard and cannot expand, it prevents the animal from growing larger. Arthropods have developed a special way to grow. They shed their exoskeleton from time to time and form another larger one. When an animal grows too large for the new exoskeleton, it will shed the exoskeleton and grown another. This process is called molting.

The arthropods are the highest evolved invertebrate animals. They probably had two common ancestors with the Annelids. (*See* EVOLUTION.) Arthropods have the most complex nervous system of the invertebrates. They have antennae which are used for touching, smelling, and hearing. Many arthropods have compound eyes. One large eye is made up of hundreds of tiny eyes that form a separate image.

The Arthropoda phylum is divided into several classes. (*See* CLASSIFICATION OF LIVING ORGANISMS.) The major classes are Insecta (insects), Crustacea (crustaceans), Arachnida (spiders), Chilopoda (centipedes), and Diplopoda (millipedes).   S.R.G./C.S.H.

**ARTICHOKE** (ärt′ ə chōk′) Artichokes are plants belonging to the composite family. They are vegetable plants that have edible buds and tubers, or roots. There are two kinds of artichokes—the globe artichoke and the Jerusalem artichoke. The globe artichoke is native to the Mediterranean region. It is grown commercially in California. Its edible, unopened flower heads, or bud clusters, grow on stalks that are about 60 to 90 cm [2 to 3 ft] high. The globe artichoke looks like a thistle. The Jerusalem artichoke is closely related to the sunflower. The edible tubers that grow on its roots look like potatoes. These tubers contain fructose, which is valuable to persons who suffer from diabetes. The Jerusalem ar-

tichoke grows to a height of 1.5 to 3.7 m [5 to 12 ft].   G.M.B./F.W.S.

Common names for the arum plant include lords-and-ladies and jack in the pulpit. The flowers grow on a spike called a spadix, which is enfolded in a hood called a spathe. Some species of arum are poisonous, but the roots of others are edible.

**ARUM FAMILY** The arum (ar′ əm) family consists of about 1,000 herbaceous plants, most of which are tropical. They are monocotyledons. Their leaves are shaped like swords. Most members of the arum family have brightly colored spathes that are easily mistaken for flowers. Most of the species wind around or onto other plants. (*See* EPIPHYTES.) Some varieties found in swampy areas of North America include skunk cabbage, jack-in-the-pulpit, and elephant's ear.

Some of these plants give off a strong odor that attracts flies and other insects. The insect is then trapped by the spathes and the leaves. The movement of the insect trying to escape pollinates the plant.

Most plants in the arum family are poisonous. The poison can be removed by cooking. The light starchy paste left after boiling the roots is called arrowroot. It is used to thicken puddings and other desserts.

A.J.C./M.H.S.

**ASBESTOS** (as bes′ təs) Asbestos is a nonmetallic mineral which may be separated into fibers. Asbestos minerals are found in many different regions. Chrysotile, the most common asbestos mineral, is found mainly in Canada and Russia.

Asbestos mineral fibers can be spun to make thread. This thread is woven into fabrics that, being made from rock, are very resistant to heat and chemicals and are good electrical insulators.

Asbestos suits are worn to fight large, very hot fires, and the fabrics have been used in theater curtains. But because the fibers and dust have been found to cause lung cancer, efforts are being made to find substitutes for asbestos in its many applications.

J.J.A./R.H.

**ASCHELMINTHES** (ask hel′ min thēz) The phylum Aschelminthes contains roundworms (class Nematoda), rotifers (class Rotifera), and several other lesser-known animals. (*See* ANIMAL KINGDOM.) The roundworms are very common animals. They are found in almost every type of environment around the world. One hectare [2.5 acres] may contain as many as six thousand million roundworms. Many roundworms are parasites. Some are found in people. One worm that is a parasite in people can grow up to 1 m [3.3 ft] in length. People get the worms by accidentally swallowing their eggs. Some roundworms are passed from dogs to humans.

Rotifers are one of the most common kinds of animal in fresh water. Most are microscopic, rarely growing larger than 0.5 mm [0.02 in]. They are important food for fishes and other aquatic species. (*See* FOOD CHAIN.)

S.R.G./C.S.H.

**ASEPSIS** (ā sep′ səs) Asepsis is the complete absence of any germs or bacteria. It is important for hospitals because germs can enter cuts or wounds and cause infections. To ensure asepsis, disease-producing germs are killed by sterilization. Operating rooms, surgical instruments, and other equipment are sterilized with steam, dry heat, or boiling water. The doctors and nurses wash with special antiseptics and wear sterile gowns and face masks. The patient's skin is cleaned with an antiseptic before surgery.

Aseptic technique has replaced the simple, less effective antiseptic methods used in the past. Asepsis has resulted in fewer infections after operations. A.J.C./J.J.F.

**ASEXUAL REPRODUCTION** (ā seksh′ wəl rē′ prə dək′ shən) Most organisms produce offspring by mating with a member of the other sex. (*See* REPRODUCTION.) Sometimes offspring can be produced without the help of a member of the other sex. This is called asexual reproduction. There are many different types of asexual reproduction.

One-celled organisms like amebae reproduce by binary fission. The original ameba simply splits in two. Before the split occurs, however, the ameba must split every part inside so that there are two of everything in the cell. When the cell splits, each half gets one of each part so that the new amebae are identical.

Another type of asexual reproduction is budding. In many lower animals, such as the cnidarians, a new animal grows off of the side of another one. Then it breaks off and becomes a separate animal.

Members of Platyhelminthes can reproduce by regeneration. If a worm of this family breaks in half, each half grows back the missing piece. After a while, there are two whole worms.

In parthenogenesis, eggs are laid without being fertilized by a male. (*See* FERTILIZATION.) The offspring are identical to the mother.

Some lower plants produce spores asexually. Spores are similar to seeds, except that they are not produced by a female plant. They are produced by a plant without a sex. The spore may grow into a male or female plant which can engage in sexual reproduction and produce a plant that will again produce spores. (*See* ALTERNATION OF GENERATION.)

Some of the higher plants, such as trees, can also reproduce asexually. If a branch of a willow tree breaks off and lands in water or·

moist soil, it can form roots and grow into another tree. This process is called vegetative propagation.

All of the offspring produced by asexual reproduction are just like their parents. They are called clones. Sexual reproduction is more common because it allows for a change between parent and offspring. This change allows living things to adapt successfully to changing conditions. (*See* ADAPTATION.) If organisms reproduced only asexually, evolution would be nearly impossible. *See also* SEX. S.R.G./E.R.L.

Leaf and seed cluster of the common ash tree.

**ASH** (ash) Ash trees are hardwood, deciduous trees which grow in North America, Europe, and Asia. They belong to the genus *Fraxinus*. They are members of the olive family. Sixteen species are native to the United States. The most common of these are the white ash, red ash, and black ash. All of these are found in the eastern states.

Ash trees may grow to be more than 30 m [100 ft] tall. Since ash is a strong hardwood, it is used in making baseball bats, oars, and the handles of shovels. A.J.C./M.H.S.

**ASPARAGUS** (a spar′ ə gəs) Asparagus is the name given to about 150 species of plants. Asparagus, naturally grown anywhere from Siberia to southern Africa, is a member of the Liliaceae, or lily family. Asparagus plants

stand by themselves or can climb onto objects, such as fences or posts. Their roots give rise to unusual leaves which look like small scales. Asparagus plants have small, greenish yellow flowers in the spring, followed by small red berries in the fall.

Asparagus can be grown in many kinds of soil. The best type of soil in which to grow asparagus year after year is a loose and light clay with a lot of organic matter. Asparagus thrives in soil too salty for most crops. It does not grow well in soil containing a lot of acid.

Three kinds of asparagus are sold as vegetables. Green spears and green spears with white butts are the kinds produced for the fresh market. Most canned asparagus is treated so that it looks whiter than the fresh kind. Asparagus is low in food value, having some protein and 94% water.

A few types of asparagus, like the *Asparagus plumosus,* are prized for their delicate leaves. They are used in corsages and in other plant arrangements. J.J.A./F.W.S.

**ASPHALT** (as′ fȯlt′) Asphalt is a black or brown mineral material used in making roads and in waterproofing roofs, water tanks, and boats. It is also used as an adhesive. Asphalt consists of hydrocarbons combined with nitrogen, sulfur, and oxygen. It can be obtained from natural deposits, called asphaltum, or from the distillation of crude petroleum. Large deposits of natural asphalt occur in Texas, Oklahoma, Utah, and California. The world's largest deposits are found in western Canada. Venezuela and Iran also have asphalt deposits.

Asphalt becomes a heavy liquid when heated. The hot liquid is mixed with crushed stone. The mixture is then spread and rolled to make road surfaces.

Asphalt is an ancient building material, used by the Babylonians and mentioned in the Bible. It was used to seal the walls of a reservoir in Pakistan in 3000 B.C.

W.R.P./J.M.

**ASS** (as) The ass is a relative of the horse. It looks like a zebra without stripes. Its height to the top of its shoulder is 90 to 150 cm [3 to 5 ft]. It can run very swiftly. It has long ears and is usually gray with a dark brown or black mane.

Wild asses live on the hot, dry plains of Africa and Asia. The onager is a wild ass of Africa. The kulan, the kiang, and the ghorkhar are wild asses of Asia. Because they are hunted for their hides and their meat, wild asses are in danger of becoming extinct.

The African wild ass is the ancestor of the donkey. Thousands of years ago, man captured the wild asses of Africa. By training them to do work, people developed a domesticated animal that was given the name donkey. Today, there are many varieties of donkeys. *See also* MULE.     G.M.B./J.J.M.

**ASSAYING** (as ā′ ying) In science, assaying is a method used to find out how much and what kinds of metals are in a rock or an unknown alloy. At one time, assaying was concerned only with finding out how much gold or silver was in an alloy.

Assays are carried out by using various means of chemical analysis. The main methods of assaying are the wet process and the dry process. In the wet process, the unknown sample is mixed with other chemicals in solution. (*See* SOLUTION AND SOLUBILITY.) The resulting products are separated and weighed. During the dry process, the sample may be crushed and pure substances sifted out. The sample may also be roasted and its products collected and measured. J.J.A./A.D.

**ASTATINE** (as′ tə tēn′) Astatine is a radioactive element. It has an atomic number of 85 and an atomic weight of about 210. Its symbol is At. It melts at 302°C [576°F] and it boils at 337°C [639°F]. It occurs in nature only in extremely small amounts. It was discovered by being made artificially. This was first done in 1940 by a team of American scientists led by Emilio Segrè. They made astatine by bombarding bismuth with alpha particles.

Astatine has twenty different isotopes. They are all very unstable. The most stable isotope is astatine-210. Even this isotope has a half-life of only 8 hours. Because it is so unstable, astatine has hardly any uses.

M.E./J.R.W

**ASTER** (as′ tər) The aster is a flowering perennial plant of the composite family. There are more than 200 known varieties in North America. The flower of this herbaceous plant is shaped like a disk. It has many thin, pointed petals which give it a starlike appearance. Its colors range from white to pink to deep blue and purple.

The aster blooms in late summer. In some warmer areas, the flowers may last until early winter. Although some asters may grow from seeds, reproduction is usually by vegetative propagation. Relatives of the aster include the chrysanthemum and the sunflower.

A.J.C./M.H.S.

**ASTEROID** (as′ tə roid′) An asteroid is an irregular lump of rock that orbits the Sun. Most asteroids travel space between the orbits of Mars and Jupiter. Two groups move with Jupiter, one ahead of the planet and the other behind. Asteroids are minor planets, much smaller than regular planets. Some asteroids are about 1.5 km [1 mi] in diameter. Ceres, the largest known asteroid, has a diameter of 784 km [490 mi]. It is nearly spherical in shape. There are about 100,000 asteroids. The majority of them are too small to be seen from the Earth. Vesta, the brightest asteroid, is the only one that can be seen without a telescope.

Some astronomers suggest that asteroids are the remains of a planet that broke up. Most astronomers, however, believe that asteroids formed at the same time as the rest of the solar system.

Eros is a small asteroid that wanders from the asteroid belt and comes closer to the Earth, within 25.6 million km [16 million mi], than any of the others. Scientists observe the movement of Eros to determine the astronomical unit, the distance between the Earth and the Sun. W.R.P./C.R.

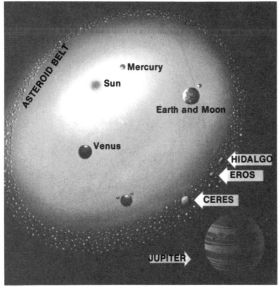

Asteroids orbit the Sun between the planets Mars and Jupiter. The largest asteroid, called Ceres, is more than 400 miles across. Next in size are Pallas and Vesta, which are about 300 and 250 miles across, respectively. Most asteroids are quite tiny. Scientists differ in their ideas about the origin of the asteroids.

**ASTHMA** (az′ mə) Asthma is a disease involving a shortness of breath and other breathing problems. It is one of the most common diseases affecting respiration. An asthmatic, or person who has asthma, may feel sudden, sharp attacks which force him to gasp for breath. Wheezing and whistling sounds, a tightness in the chest, and steady coughing are all signs of asthma.

Asthma is caused by a blocking of the bronchial tubes in the lungs. This blocking is caused by shrinking of the bronchial muscles, swelling of the membranes lining these muscles, and the presence of thick mucus called phlegm. The lungs of a person with asthma become narrowed.

Allergic bronchial asthma is the most common type of this disease. Bronchial asthma is caused by an adverse reaction to things such as house dust, pollen, and certain foods. Asthma is often linked with hay fever, another type of allergy. However, with asthma, the allergic reaction affects the bronchial tubes. With hay fever, the reaction affects the nasal passages. Different kinds of asthma may do harm to other parts of the body.

Asthma attacks often occur after heavy physical work or when a person is emotionally upset. An infection of the nose and throat can trigger an attack. A drastic change in the weather may also cause an attack.

A physician identifies asthma by physical examination and allergy skin tests. These tests may tell what substances a patient is allergic to. Most doctors prescribe drugs such as epinephrine or ephedrine to relieve symptoms of asthma. Patients with very serious cases of asthma may need to take ACTH or cortisol. Some doctors prescribe small doses or injections of the asthma-causing substances. The doctor slowly increases the strength of these injections until the patient's body has built up a natural resistance to the substances. J.J.A./J.J.F.

**ASTROLABE** (as′ trə lāb′) An astrolabe is an instrument that was used by ancient Greek ship navigators and astronomers. It measured the altitude, or height, of stars and planets above the horizon in degrees, minutes, and seconds. (*See* MEASUREMENT.) Ship captains used this information to navigate their ships. Today, navigators use an instrument called a sextant to obtain the altitudes of celestial bodies. The sextant is a highly improved version of the astrolabe. *See also* NAVIGATION; QUADRANT. W.R.P./J.V.P.

**ASTROLOGY** (ə sträl′ ə jē) Astrology is an unscientific study of the moon, the sun, the planets, and the stars. It is based on a belief that these heavenly bodies influence human affairs. Astrology began more than 3,000 years ago in Babylonia. It was the beginning of the science of astronomy. Even though astrology has no scientific basis, many people still believe in it. Most scientists say that modern astrology is not based on scientific fact.

Ancient astrology had some scientific value because it was the first study of the heavenly bodies. The astrology of ancient Egypt identified the 12 constellations that are the signs of the zodiac. People who practice astrology use the zodiac to predict the future. These people are called astrologers. (*See* ZODIAC.)                                    G.M.B./C.R.

**ASTRONAUTICS** (as′ trə nȯt′ iks) Astronautics is the science of flight in space beyond the earth's atmosphere. It applies knowledge gained from physics, metallurgy, jet propulsion, and human biology to the de-

This Soviet Elektron 2 satellite was launched in 1964 to study the earth's radiation belts. Atomic particles in these belts were found to produce X rays that could be harmful to astronauts.

Space laboratories of both the United States and the U.S.S.R. have shown that it is possible to live and work in space for long periods of time. In the future, more sophisticated space stations would be possible. Someday there may even be space stations like the one (below) from the motion picture *The Empire Strikes Back*.

The top photograph shows flight controllers in the mission operations control room at the Johnson Space Center in Houston, Texas. The large monitor shows part of the space shuttle *Columbia*. Astronaut Edwin E. Aldrin, Jr., (bottom) is shown walking on the moon. Contact between the astronauts and mission control has been important to the success of the flights.

sign, construction, and operation of spacecraft. Astronautics deals with ways to control and track the flight of spacecraft. It also deals with the unusual conditions (such as weightlessness) that crews experience during flight outside the earth's gravity.

Astronautics is a relatively recent science. It had its beginnings in the science of aeronautics, which deals with flight within the earth's atmosphere. Because vehicles designed for spaceflight also have to be able to operate within the earth's atmosphere (during launch and reentry), astronautics and aeronautics are overlapping sciences. Astronautics deals mainly with ways to use jet propulsion to control the direction and speed of a spacecraft when it is largely free of the earth's gravitational pull.

The first recorded use of the word *astronautics* was in 1927. The development of a distinct science of space flight occurred rapidly after the Soviet Union launched the first two Sputnik satellites in 1957. In July 1969, the United States successfully sent two astronauts, in the spacecraft *Apollo II*, to the moon. By 1975, more than a hundred space missions had been successfully flown, including seven moon landings. The first reusable manned spacecraft—the space shuttle *Columbia*—was successfully tested by the United States in 1981.

As astronautics rapidly became a fully developed science, the purposes of each new spaceflight became more ambitious. Spacecraft have been fitted with many kinds of instruments for gathering information about the environment of space. All of the moon's surface has been mapped in great detail by both manned and unmanned spacecraft. Television cameras in unmanned spacecraft have sent closeup pictures of Mars, Jupiter, and other planets in our solar system. Various kinds of scientific detectors mounted on space probes have sent back to earth information about such things as weather, temperature, and biological conditions. These probes can be controlled by radio. Their flight path can be changed, their cameras aimed, and their equipment turned on and off.

Astronautics has developed satellites whose purposes include military reconnaissance, long-distance communications, radiation measurement, and astronomical observation. Some of these satellites remain in constant orbit, providing a useful service to us on earth. Navigation satellites send radio signals that can help a ship at sea to check its course. Communications satellites make it possible to send live television pictures over very long distances.

Astronautics has provided much new information for astronomers. Satellites can take photographs of the sun and planets without the distortion that occurs when the photographs are taken from earth. Unmanned satellites equipped with scientific detectors can obtain information that cannot yet be obtained by manned spacecraft.

Astronautics will eventually make it possible to establish a base on the moon, orbit a permanent space station, and even send an expedition to Mars. *See also* ASTRONOMY; SPACE TRAVEL; WEIGHTLESSNESS. P.G.Z./G.D.B.

**ASTRONOMICAL UNIT** (as′ trə näm′ i kəl yü′ nət) The astronomical unit is used by astronomers and astrophysicists to measure distances in outer space. It is approximately equal to 149,600,000 km [93,000,000 mi], the mean distance between earth and the sun. *See also* LIGHT-YEAR; PARSEC. G.M.B./J.VP.

# ASTRONOMY

Astronomy (ə strän′ ə mē) is the scientific study of all the things of the universe that are outside of earth and its atmosphere. Scientists who work in astronomy are called astronomers. They study the sky with telescopes, radar, spectroscopes, cameras, artificial satellites, and spacecraft. Astronomers gather information about everything outside of the earth's atmosphere. They also provide information for navigation and for the measurement of time on earth.

**Ancient roots of astronomy**  Astronomy is thousands of years old. It has its roots in astrology, the unscientific study of heavenly bodies. In ancient Babylonia, the sun, the moon, and the stars were studied to establish a measurement of time. In ancient Egypt, when certain stars appeared at certain locations, the people knew that it was time for the river Nile to flood. For example, the appearance of the constellation Aquarius was a warning. It meant preparations for the flood should begin. (*See* CONSTELLATION; ZODIAC.) In Central and South America, the Mayan and Incan civilizations based their architecture on astrological observations.

Astronomy began in ancient Greece. About 2,600 years ago, Pythagoras guessed that the earth was a sphere at the center of the universe. About 800 years later, another Greek scholar, Ptolemy, wrote a book that was to be the basis of astronomy for the next 1,400 years. The mistake made by almost all of the early astronomers was to think that the earth was at the center of the universe. They thought that the sun, moon, stars, and planets revolved around earth, which didn't move at all.

**Beginnings of modern astronomy**  Modern astronomy began with the work of Nicolaus Copernicus, in the 16th century. In 1543, he established that the earth moved around the sun. Copernicus explained that all planets orbited the sun and corrected Ptolemy's idea of the universe. Later in the 16th century, Tycho Brahe, of Denmark, spent many years studying the stars and the planets. He kept careful records of the positions of the stars and planets. Brahe died before he was able to complete his work. Another astronomer,

Johannes Kepler, used Brahe's work to discover how planets moved around the sun. Kepler was a mathematician. He was able to show that each planet traveled in an elliptical, or oval-shaped, orbit around the sun.

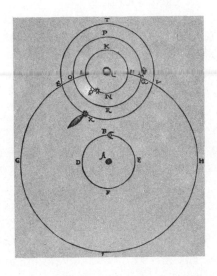

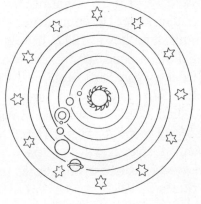

The top drawing shows Tycho Brahe's theory of the solar system. This astronomer put the earth at the center but had all the other planets revolve around the sun. Eventually, astronomers accepted Copernicus' theory (lower drawing).

**Galileo and Newton**  At the same time that Kepler was calculating the orbits of the planets, Galileo was developing the telescope. This instrument enabled man to see the sky better than he had ever done before. In 1610, Galileo observed the moons of Jupiter and the moonlike phases of Venus. After Galileo's death, in 1642, the English astronomer and mathematician Sir Isaac New-

A seventeenth century astronomer studies the stars.

The picture shows a restoration of an ancient observatory in India. Architectural shapes measured positions of sun and stars.

ton made the most important discovery since the time of Copernicus. Newton's three laws of gravitation explained the movements of all heavenly bodies. He proved, for example, that gravitation controls the orbit of the moon. Newton also invented the spectroscope, which was to become a valuable tool for astronomers.

**Discovery of the planets**   Using the discoveries of Copernicus, Brahe, Kepler, Newton, and others, later astronomers located planets that had never before been found. In 1781, Sir William Herschel discovered Uranus. Neptune was discovered by J. G. Galle in 1846. Early in the 20th century, Sir Percival Lowell predicted the existence of Pluto. In 1930, the planet was sighted by C. W. Tombaugh at Lowell Observatory, in Flagstaff, Ariz. The discovery of Pluto established the nine principal planets of the solar system. Five of the nine planets had been known since ancient times. These are, listed by their closeness to the sun: Mercury, Venus, Mars, Jupiter, and Saturn. Earth orbits the sun between Venus and Mars. Copernicus had identified the earth as a planet in 1543. (*See* SOLAR SYSTEM.) Ceres was the first minor planet, or asteroid, to be discovered. It was found by astronomers in 1801. By the middle of the 20th century, astronomers had identified about 1,600 minor planets. They continue to find them by careful study of photographs of the sky. (*See* ASTEROID.)

**Stars**   While some astronomers searched for planets, other astronomers searched for stars. In the early 1800s, Joseph Fraunhofer became one of the first astronomers to use Newton's spectroscope to examine starlight.

A 3,000-year-old picture of the universe. The body of the goddess Nut forms the star-filled sky. Earth god Qeb is at her feet.

His work led to a new branch of astronomy called astrophysics. (*See* ASTROPHYSICS.)

**Photography**  Photography is an important tool of astronomy. In 1840, astronomers first photographed the moon. By 1850, photographs of the stars had become possible. Today, astronomers use cameras that are very complex and sensitive. These cameras are able to photograph stars that cannot be seen by the eye, even with a telescope. In the United States, astronomers at Harvard University have been adding information to a catalog of stars since 1885. It is called the Henry Draper Catalogue. In contains photographs and measurements of more than 400,000 stars.

**Meteorites and comets**  Astronomers also study meteorites and comets. Meteorites are meteors that have landed on the earth. Some weigh more than a ton. In Arizona, there is a crater 1,210 m [4,000 ft] across and 183 m [600 ft] deep that scientists believe was caused by the impact of a meteor. Comets may also strike the earth. In 1908, one exploded over a part of Russia called Siberia with a force so great that tremors were recorded throughout the world.

**Telescopes and radiotelescopes**  Telescopes are the instruments most often used by astronomers. With the largest reflecting telescope in the world, astronomers at the Palomar Observatory in California are able to photograph stars that are a billion light-years away. The world's largest refracting telescope is at the Yerkes Observatory in Wisconsin. Radio telescopes are used to receive and record radio waves that are sent out by objects in space. In the 1960s, astronomers discovered new kinds of objects in space by using radio astronomy. (*See* PULSAR; QUASAR.) In 1965, astronomers used radar to learn how long it takes for Mercury and Venus to turn on their axes.

**Recent developments**  The space technology of the 20th century has led to great advances in astronomy. In 1947, the United States launched a rocket to take the first photographs outside of the atmosphere. In 1959, a Russian space probe televised the first pictures of the side of the moon that is always turned away from the earth. In the 1960s, the United States was receiving information from spacecraft that had been launched to pass near Mars and Venus.

A student who wants to become an astronomer should concentrate on mathematics and science in high school. Most astronomers are teachers at colleges and universities. Some astronomers work for government and industrial organizations. *See also* COSMOLOGY; HALLEY'S COMET; SPACE TRAVEL.

G.M.B./C.R.

**ASTROPHYSICS** (as′ trə fiz′ iks) Astrophysics deals with the physical and chemical makeup of celestial, or heavenly, bodies. It applies the theories and methods of physics to determine the structure of stars and to solve other problems in astronomy.

Astrophysics is primarily an observational science. It includes the study of the kinds of energy given off by the sun and the other stars, as well as by planets and nebulae. In particular, it is the study of the light and electromagnetic radiation given off by the bodies.

By analyzing the light coming from a star, an astrophysicist can determine what physical elements are present in the body of the star. This analysis is made with a spectroscope, which converts the light waves given off by a star into the various colors they contain. The density and range of the colors in the spectrum are part of the evidence the astrophysicist uses.

Most stars give off radio waves and X rays. Astrophysics uses techniques of radio astronomy and X-ray astronomy. Evidence gained by study of magnetic fields, light waves, radio waves, and X rays emitted by stars has enabled astronomers to calculate such things as a star's mass, temperature, and inner structure.

Astrophysics also deals with distances between stars and with the motion of stars, as well as that of planets and their satellites. It helps astronomers to make maps of galaxies. The instruments used for this purpose include telescopes, photoelectric cells, radio antennas, and computers.

Space exploration has greatly increased the amount of information available to astronomers. Telescopes and other astrophysical instruments carried outside the earth's atmosphere by balloons and satellites have enabled astronomers to view the sun's atmosphere and surface clearly.

Instruments carried by satellites have greatly increased the ability of astronomers to collect information. They have also led to the discovery of unusual astronomical bodies—black holes, pulsars, and quasars—whose natures are being closely studied. Astrophysicists are giving close attention to quasars, for instance, because quasars are the most distant star-like galaxies visible from the earth. A quasar is faint blue in color when viewed through a telescope. Study of the light of quasars indicates that they are moving away from the earth's galaxy (the Milky Way) at

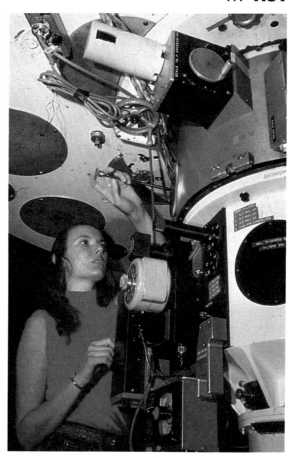

This astrophysicist is using a spectrograph with a large telescope to examine radiation from space.

nearly the speed of light. (*See* RED SHIFT.) The brightness of a quasar has been calculated as more than that of 100 galaxies combined.

What is intriguing to astronomers is the fact that light reaching the earth from quasars was emitted billions of years ago. One of the difficulties in studying very distant heavenly bodies is that only evidence that existed in the past can be observed. We cannot directly determine anything about the present reality of even the closest stars to our galaxy. That is because their light—which is where we get evidence about them—takes so long to reach earth. Light from the sun, for example, takes about eight minutes to reach the earth. But light from distant stars may take millions of years to reach the earth.

The light emitted by a star can give the

astrophysicist information about its surface. But what the inside of a star is like must be inferred, using the sciences of physics and chemistry. For example, if the surface temperature of a star is 5,000 degrees, the inside temperature will be millions of degrees. By taking into account a star's weight, mass, surface temperature, and light, an astrophysicist can calculate its approximate age and may even be able to trace its probable history. *See also* ASTRONOMY; BLACK HOLE; COSMOLOGY; GALAXY; SOLAR SYSTEM.          P.G.Z./G.D.B.

**ATMOSPHERE** (at′ məs fir′) The atmosphere is the mass of gases which surrounds the earth. It is about 800 km [500 mi] high. Its total weight is almost 5½ million billion metric tons [6 million billion tons].

The force of gravity holds the earth's atmosphere around the earth. Other planets in our solar system have a gravitational force strong enough to hold an atmosphere in place. Their atmospheres are different from the one that surrounds earth. Earth's atmosphere is made up of dust, gases, and water vapor. Two of its gases, nitrogen and oxygen, make up 99% of the volume of air. Air is necessary to most life. Scientists are concerned about the effects of air pollution because of the limited supply of air available to us.

The atmosphere protects the earth from harm. It prevents too much ultraviolet light from reaching the earth by acting as a filter between the earth and the sun. Acting as a blanket, the atmosphere keeps the earth from losing too much heat at night. It also protects the earth from meteors and cosmic rays.

The atmosphere changes as it gets higher and further away from earth. The higher it goes, the thinner it gets because the molecules of its gases are farther apart. The air is so thin above 7,500 m [25,000 ft] that travelers must have extra oxygen to survive.

To help describe the differences among the levels of the atmosphere, scientists have divided it into four layers. Starting with the layer next to the earth's surface, they are the troposphere, the stratosphere, the ionosphere, and the exosphere.

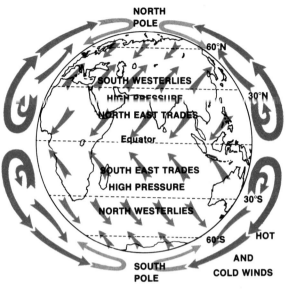

World wind belts are caused by heated air rising from the equator and moving outward. Colder air from the polar regions moves in to replace it.

**Troposphere**   About 75% of the entire mass of the atmosphere is in the troposphere. It starts at the earth's surface and extends outward to an altitude of 8 to 16 km [5 to 10 mi]. It is the layer in which all of our weather occurs.

The troposphere is about 80% nitrogen and about 20% oxygen, with small amounts of carbon dioxide. Most of the water and dust in the atmosphere is to be found in this layer.

About 45% of the sun's radiation falling on earth is absorbed by the ground; 18% is absorbed by the atmosphere; and 37% is reflected back into space. Most of the 18% absorbed by the atmosphere is absorbed by the carbon dioxide, water vapor, and dust in the troposphere. The carbon dioxide, water vapor, and dust are thicker near the ground. This is why the warmest temperatures in the troposphere are to be found near the earth. As the height of the troposphere increases, its temperature drops at the rate of 7°C per km [20°F per mi].

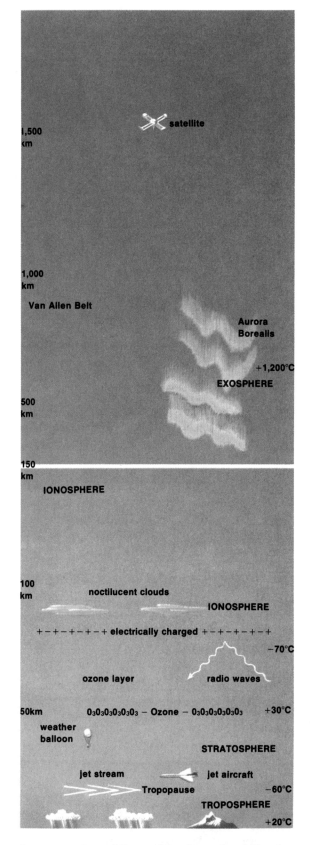

A cross section of the earth's atmosphere showing the main regions and their average temperatures. There are no clear-cut boundaries between the layers of the atmosphere.

In the upper troposphere, unusual winds are found. These are narrow and fast-moving currents of air called jet streams. In and beyond the upper troposphere, the atmosphere contains too little oxygen to support life.

The uppermost limit of the troposphere is called the tropopause. Its altitude varies from 8 km [5 mi] in some places to 18 km [11 mi]. Its temperature also varies, from $-51°C$ [$-60°F$] at the lowest altitudes to $-79°C$ [$-110°F$] at the highest.

**Stratosphere** The stratosphere begins 16 km [10 mi] above the earth and extends out to a height of 80 km [50 mi]. There are only a few clouds in the stratosphere. They are made up mostly of ice crystals. These crystals form on the small particles of dust that remain when meteors burn up in the atmosphere. The only winds in the stratosphere are jet streams and other fast moving winds. Jet streams blow toward the east. Because they help planes to fly faster and to save fuel, pilots like to fly them on long trips.

Jet pilots also prefer to fly in the stratosphere to avoid storms in the troposphere below. Airplanes flying in the stratosphere may leave behind trails like long, thin, white clouds called contrails, which is short for condensation trails. They are made up of freezing water from a plane's exhaust.

The upper stratosphere is warmer than the other layers of the stratosphere. This is because its ozone filters the energy of the ultraviolet light from the sun. Because it controls the amount of ultraviolet light that reaches the earth, the ozone layer is very important. Scientists are concerned about its possible pollution by the exhaust of supersonic jets, as well as by chemicals in aerosol sprays used in the home.

**Ionosphere** The ionosphere begins at an altitude of 80 km [50 mi] and ends about 480 km [300 mi] above the earth. It is called the ionosphere because the sun's radiation ionizes most of the molecules of its thin air. (*See* IONS; IONIZATION.) The ionosphere is important in radio astronomy and in communications with artificial satellites. It allows short, high frequency waves to pass through. It is important in radio communications because it reflects low and medium frequency radio waves back to the ground, in much the same way a mirror reflects light.

Sometimes the ionosphere is disturbed by particles from the sun. These disturbances cause glowing lights in the sky called auroras. (*See* AURORA.)

**Exosphere**　The exosphere is the outermost layer of the atmosphere. It begins 480 km [300 mi] above the earth, but its boundary with outer space has not yet been clearly defined. The outer parts of the exosphere contain mostly hydrogen and helium gases.

The exosphere has a high temperature because the few atoms and molecules in its very thin air are able to move about very rapidly.

**Pressure and circulation of the atmosphere**　Look at the top of a desk. Imagine a column of air pressing on it that is about 800 km [500 mi] high. The total amount of weight on the desk top is called atmospheric pressure. At sea level, the atmosphere has a pressure of 1.03 kg per sq cm [14.7 lbs per sq in].

There are many forces that account for the circulation of the atmosphere. One force is the result of the sun warming the air near the equator more than it warms the air at the poles. The uneven temperatures make the atmosphere circulate, carrying air along the ground from colder to warmer regions.

Atmospheric pressure varies from one region on earth to another. Air near the ground tends to flow from areas where pressure is higher to areas where it is lower. Circulation results when the differences in pressure even themselves out.　　　　H.G./C.R.

**ATMOSPHERE**　(unit)　An atmosphere (at′ mə sfir′) is a unit of atmospheric pressure. It equals 6.7 kg per square inch [14.7 lb per square inch]. That is the pressure produced by a column of mercury in an upright tube that is 76 cm [30 in] high. An atmosphere is also equal to 1,013 millibars, and 101.325 newtons per square meter. Air has a pressure of approximately one atmosphere at sea level. *See also* BAROMETER.

W.R.P./R.W.L.

Formation of an atoll. Above, a volcano rises above the level of the sea, forming an island. A reef of coral forms around the volcano. Above right, as the volcano begins to settle beneath the waves, the coral reef builds up higher. The coral organisms can survive only near the surface. Right, even though the volcano may become completely worn away, a circular atoll is left, enclosing a lagoon. Many such atolls may be found in the Pacific Ocean.

**ATOLL** (a′ tòl′) An atoll is a ring or horse-shoe-shaped group of coral islands surrounding a body of sea water. Atolls are found in tropical seas where corals and algae grow best. The water must be shallow, with lots of sunlight upon it. The lower limit for coral growth is between 60 m [197 ft] and 90 m [295 ft]. A very unusual drilling at the Eniwetok Atoll in the Marshall Islands discovered at least 1,525 m [5,000 ft] of coral.

There are a number of theories why coral can form to such a great depth. One suggestion is that sea levels have slowly risen, allowing coral to form in further layers. Another theory explains the formation of layers of coral as the result of the slow sinking of land beneath the seas.          J.J.A./W.R.S.

# ATOM

An atom (at′ əm) is the smallest part of an element having all the properties of that element. All matter, anything that has mass, is made up of atoms. It is difficult to realize how extremely small an atom is. For example, this page is more than a million atoms thick.

Atoms are made up of smaller particles. Every atom consists of a central part called a nucleus. Around the nucleus there are up to about a hundred electrons. The nucleus is very small compared to the size of an atom. If the diameter of an atom were the size of a football field (91.44 m or 100 yards), the nucleus would be the size of a pea. In this sense, an atom consists mostly of space.

The nucleus is made up of two kinds of particles, protons and neutrons. Their masses are almost equal and they are both about 1,850 times heavier than an electron. This means that almost all the mass of an atom is concentrated in the nucleus. The mass of the nucleus is less than the mass of its protons and neutrons. This is because when the parti-

cles form a nucleus, some of their mass is converted to energy to hold them together. The neutrons have no electric charge but the proton is positively charged and the electron has an equal negative charge. Usually an atom has equal numbers of protons and electrons. This makes the atom electrically neutral.

The difference between one kind of atom and another lies in the number of protons in the nucleus. There are as many different kinds of atoms as there are elements.

The number of electrons moving around the nucleus is the same as the number of protons inside it. Hydrogen has one proton in the nucleus and one electron outside it. Uranium has a nucleus containing 92 protons and therefore 92 electrons surrounding it. These electrons are flying around the nucleus at great speeds. Their arrangement is very complicated and it is difficult to know where any electron is at any moment. But a simple way of thinking about them is to imagine them to be in orbit around the nucleus, like a spacecraft orbiting the earth. These orbits are called shells. There are several different shells. The further away the shell is from the nucleus, the more electrons it can hold. The shell closest to the nucleus can only hold two electrons. This shell may only have one electron, as it does in a hydrogen atom. When this shell has two electrons, as in helium, the shell is said to be filled. The second shell can hold up to eight electrons, the third up to 18, and so on. The electrons in an atom always arrange themselves so that the shells nearest the nucleus are filled first.

The outer electrons are responsible for the chemical properties of the atom. Atoms are most stable when their outer shells are filled. If they have an unfilled outer shell they try to become more stable by forming molecules. Some atoms, like helium, do not have any unfilled shells. These atoms therefore do not form ordinary molecules. These elements occur in nature as single atoms. They are said to be monatomic. Atoms of some other ele-

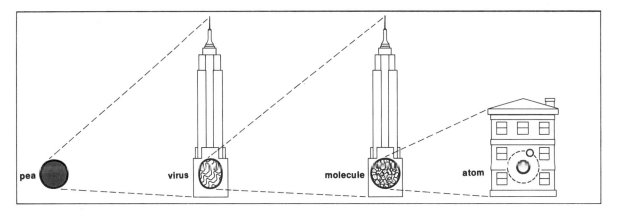

If a pea were magnified to the size of the Empire State Building, a virus on that pea would be about the size of the original pea. If this virus were then similarly enlarged, a medium-sized molecule would be pea-sized. Magnified to the size of a three-story building, an atom in the molecule would be pea-sized.

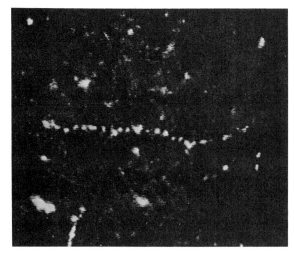

This is an actual photograph of radiation emitted by radioactive thorium atoms. The camera caught a line of those atoms.
The line passing across the center of this pictures is made up of radioactive thorium atoms.

ments, such as hydrogen, are joined together in pairs by bonds. Such molecules are said to be diatomic.

Sometimes an atom loses an electron. It then becomes positively charged. An atom can also gain an electron and become negatively charged. An atom that gains or loses an electron is said to be ionized. The charged atom is called an ion. Since unlike charges attract each other, positive ions attract nega-

tive ions. When they come together they form a chemical bond. This kind of bond is called an ionic or electrovalent bond. When atoms combine in this way they both end up with completed outer shells.

Atoms can also bind together by sharing electrons. The bond formed is called a covalent bond. The electrons spend part of the time with one atom and part of the time with the other. In this way, they can make the outer shells of both atoms full.

**Isotopes**   Just as atoms can have different numbers of electrons and protons, they can also have different numbers of neutrons in the nucleus. Atoms having the same number of protons but a different number of neutrons from other atoms are still atoms of the same element. But they are said to be isotopes of that element. For example, hydrogen has two isotopes called deuterium and tritium. Normal hydrogen has one proton in its nucleus. Deuterium has one proton and one neutron in its nucleus. Tritium has one proton and two neutrons. They are all forms of hydrogen and they all have the same chemical properties. This is because they all have only one electron.

**Investigating the atom**   Atoms are too small to be seen in an optical microscope or in an electron microscope. They can, however, be seen with a field ion microscope. The atoms appear only as patches of light with little shape. Scientists do not have to see atoms in order to learn about them. Chemists can discover how atoms react together by seeing how large samples of substances react together. Physicists can find out how atoms are arranged in crystal lattices. They do this by passing X rays through the crystals and studying the pattern of X rays after passing through the atoms. The spectrum of light produced in a spectroscope gives information on the arrangement of electrons inside an atom. In a bubble chamber, the tracks of moving particles can be photographed. (*See* AC-CELERATOR, PARTICLE.)

**Atomic energy**   Atomic energy is produced by the nucleus of an atom. Thus it is better called nuclear energy. It can be obtained by fission or by fusion. In fission, the nuclei of large atoms break apart to form smaller nuclei. When they split, the nuclei lose some of their mass. The lost mass has been converted to energy. Fusion occurs when the nuclei of small atoms, such as hydrogen, combine together to form helium with a release of energy. *See also* NUCLEAR PHYSICS.          M.E./A.I.

**ATOMIC NUMBER** (ə täm′ ik nəm′ bər) An atomic number is the number of protons in the nucleus of an atom. Since each proton in the nucleus has one positive electric charge, the total number of positive electric charges in the nucleus is equal to the atomic

The drawings at the left below show molecules that contain only one kind of atom. The atoms of helium occur singly. It is a monatomic gas.

The atomic structure of hydrogen, carbon, and thorium. Hydrogen has the simplest atom, consisting of a nucleus (red ball) that contains one proton and one electron (black dot). The nucleus of the carbon atom contains six protons and six neutrons. It has six electrons arranged in two shells—two in the first shell and four in the outer one. The nucleus of thorium has 90 protons and 142 neutrons. Its 90 electrons occupy seven shells, with two in the outer shell.

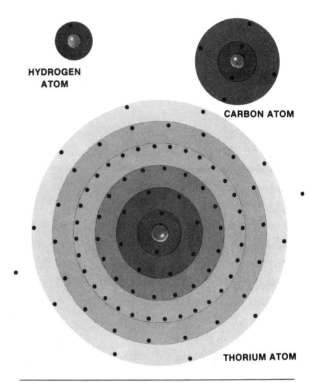

HYDROGEN ATOM

CARBON ATOM

THORIUM ATOM

Isotopes are atoms of the same element that have different numbers of neutrons in the nucleus. The table shows details of isotopes of hydrogen. To identify each isotope, a symbol is used, with numerals indicating the number of particles in the nucleus as well as the number of electrons. Note that the number of electrons and protons is the same for the three isotopes. This is true of all isotopes.

Helium gas always consists of single atoms

Hydrogen gas usually consists of pairs of atoms sharing their electrons

Ozone gas consists of triplets of oxygen atoms sharing their electrons

| ISOTOPE | SYMBOL | PROTONS | NEUTRONS | ELECTRONS | ATOM |
|---|---|---|---|---|---|
| Hydrogen | $^{1}_{1}$H | 1 | 0 | 1 | |
| Deuterium | $^{2}_{1}$H | 1 | 1 | 1 | |
| Tritium | $^{3}_{1}$H | 1 | 2 | 1 | |

number. This number is the same as the number of electrons surrounding the nucleus of a neutral atom. Each of these electrons has one negative charge.

Every element has a different atomic number. This provides a way to identify any element. In the periodic table, the elements are arranged in order according to atomic number. *See also* ELECTRON; ELEMENT; NEUTRON; PROTON.               J.J.A./A.D.

**ATOMIC WEIGHT** (ə täm′ ik wāt) Atomic weight is the weight, or mass, of one atom of an element compared to the weight of one atom of carbon-12. The atomic weight of an atom is found by adding the number of its protons (atomic number) and the number of its neutrons. Carbon-12 has 6 protons and 6 neutrons.

Scientists originally chose oxygen as the standard against which to measure atomic weights because oxygen was so common. However, because the element carbon combines readily with most other elements, it was chosen in 1960 as the standard.

Atomic weights of elements are not given as whole numbers. For instance, the atomic weight of carbon is 12.011. This figure represents the average weight of all carbon atoms, not the weight of a single atom. The weight is greater than 12 because it includes isotopes of carbon.

Atomic weight is also called mass number or mass unit. A neutron weighs about 1 mass unit. A mass unit is very small. It is equal to $1.660 \times 10^{-24}$ grams, or .00000000000000000000000166 grams. Because a mass unit is so small, atomic weights are given as numbers that show a relative value. Relative value tells us that sulfur, with an atomic weight of 32, is twice as heavy as oxygen, which has an atomic weight of 16.
                                        R.H.H./J.M.

**ATP** ATP, adenosine triphosphate, is an important chemical substance that is usually formed in the mitochondria of living cells. (*See* MITOCHONDRIA.) ATP stores energy for use within the cells. When energy is needed for metabolic activities such as protein synthesis, nerve, gland, or muscle function, ATP supplies it. (*See* METABOLISM.)

ATP contains three phosphate molecules that are held together by energy-rich chemical bonds. When energy is required, one of these bonds breaks, releasing energy. One phosphate splits off, leaving ADP (adenosine diphosphate). This reaction (ATP → ADP + P + energy) is controlled by enzymes. (*See* ENZYME.)

The cells constantly renew their supplies of ATP. Animals form the energy-rich ATP from ADP by using energy released from digested food. (*See* RESPIRATION.) Plants renew their ATP supplies during photosynthesis by using energy from sunlight. (*See* PHOTOSYNTHESIS.) Although ATP is usually formed in the mitochondria, it is released for use by any part of the cell. *See also* CELL. A.J.C./E.R.L.

**AUDUBON, JOHN JAMES** (1785–1851) John James Audubon (ô′ dù bən) was one of the first American naturalists and ornithologists to study and paint birds of the United States. (*See* ORNITHOLOGY.) His drawings and paintings were of birds in their natural surroundings.

He painted some 1,055 life-sized pictures and had them published in London as *The Birds of America*. Original copies of this book are now very valuable. They are found mostly in large libraries and museums.

Audubon did much to publicize the value of wildlife in the United States. The National Audubon Society was named in his honor and is still one of the major wildlife societies in the United States.               P.G.C./D.G.F.

**AUK** (ȯk) Auks are seabirds belonging to the family Alcidae. They have short wings, and legs set far back on their bodies. They are excellent swimmers and divers, using their wings as paddles and their feet as rudders. Auks are usually black and white. They spend the winters feeding on fish and plankton in the northern Atlantic and Pacific Oceans. In the spring, huge colonies come ashore, nesting in the cliffs. The female lays one or two eggs in cracks in the rocks. The parents stay with their young until they are well-grown.

One species, the great auk (*Alca impennis*), became extinct in 1844. This bird could not fly. It was hunted ruthlessly for its feathers and meat. The existing 21 species of alcids are about a third the size of the great auk, and are able to fly. The little auk (*Plautus alle*), or dovekie, is about 20 cm [8 in] long and feeds on plankton. (*See* PLANKTON.) Other small auks are called auklets or sea sparrows. *See also* BIRD.                                         A.J.C./M.L.

Auks are water birds with wings that work well as paddles under water. These birds are poor flyers.

**AURIGA** (ȯ rī′ gǝ) Auriga is the name of a constellation in the northern hemisphere. The last of the autumn constellations, its appearance over the horizon is a sign that winter soon will begin. It lies along the Milky Way. It includes Capella, which is the sixth brightest star in the sky. Capella is 80 times as bright as the sun. Because it is 45 light-years away from the earth, it just looks like a bright star. Capella is also called the Goat. The Auriga constellation is also called the Charioteer.                                    G.M.B./C.R.

**AURORA** (ǝ rōr ǝ) The aurora is a natural display of light in the sky. Occasionally, the night sky in the northern hemisphere glows with bright green, red, blue, and yellow colors. This is called the aurora borealis. The aurora australis is the name for the same display that occurs in the southern hemisphere. The auroras are usually located near the North or South Poles at heights of 80 to 160 km [50 to 100 mi]. Some may be as high as 1,000 km [600 mi].

When there is an increase in sunspot activity, the clouds of charged atomic particles that the sun sends out increase in strength. (*See* SOLAR WIND.) These solar particles travel through space in all directions. As they enter the earth's atmosphere, the magnetism at the poles changes the direction and speed of the particles. These particles then collide with air molecules in the cold, thin upper atmosphere. This causes colored light. This process may continue for hours, often lighting the sky for an entire evening.                               A.J.C./C.R.

This picture of the aurora borealis was taken by NASA in 1969. The studies done that year greatly advanced knowledge of this phenomenon.      NASA

**AUSTRALOID** (ȯs′ trǝ lȯid′) Australoid is the name given to a race of primitive people found in Australia and Tasmania. Australoid people have dark skin and slender bodies. They have curly hair and large bushy eyebrows, large lower jaws and large teeth. The males have heavy body hair and tend to become bald in middle age.

In Australia, Australoid people are known as aborigines. Before the Europeans came to Australia in the eighteenth century, there were 500 different tribes of aborigines. The lifestyle of the Europeans clashed with the simple ways of the aborigines. Soon, fighting and killing became common. The aborigines were no match for the weapons of the Europeans and were driven into the bush country, or Outback.

In the 1920s, areas of land called reserves were set aside for the aborigines. Now there are only a few thousand aborigines living in the primitive style of their ancestors. There are around 100,000 full-blooded aborigines and those of mixed blood living in cities and small towns. The Australian Federal Office of Aboriginal Affairs has been established to protect the rights of the aborigines.

There are no longer any Australoid people in Tasmania. They were hunted down by Europeans in the eighteenth and nineteenth centuries. *See also* ANTHROPOLOGY.

A.J.C./S.O.

This robot picks up a rough casting, takes it to various stations, and then puts away the finished, inspected casting.

**AUTOMATION** (ȯt′ ə mā′ shən) Simply stated, automation is the use of machines to run other machines. It is a way of making a device, a process, or a system operate auto-matically. Human effort is not involved in the actual work. Once a person has planned what the machine should do and has turned on the power, the machine does the rest. Unlike workers whom they replace, such machines do not make mistakes, get tired, or take time off for sickness. But they cannot think for themselves or make judgments. They can only do what people have instructed them to do.

Because the word *automation* first came into general use in mid-twentieth century, it may seem that automation is a new trend. It is not. In fact, some scholars believe it to be simply an extension of the mechanization that started in the Industrial Revolution of the eighteenth century. The automatic machine-control of complex systems so commonplace today really began in the steam-operated textile machines of eighteenth-century England. The steam engines that powered those machines were fitted with automatic valves and governors that controlled their speed. In 1801, Joseph Marie Jacquard, a Frenchman, suggested the use of cards with a pattern of holes punched in them. He used the cards to automate a loom. Today, similar cards are used to control various kinds of automated machines. Early in the twentieth century, American industry used automated machines in the mass production of automobiles. Because machines often surpassed human workers in job performance, many other industries turned to automation.

Science and technology soon responded to the call of business and industry for faster and more efficient production. New scientific discoveries, especially in electronics, changed the modern world much as the inventions of the Industrial Revolution had done. Advances in radio, television, telecommunications, and aviation helped lay the groundwork for the dawning of the space age in the 1950s.

Space travel posed a new set of problems. Automation was the answer to many of them.

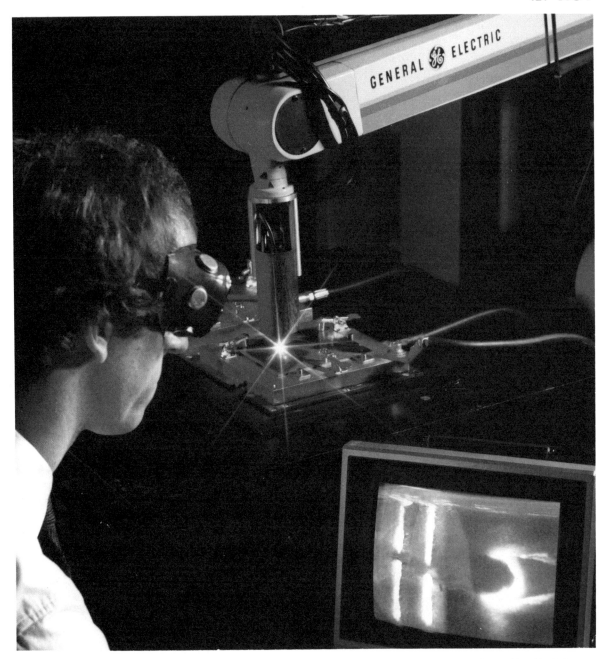

Two laser beams enable the welding robot above to steer itself along an irregularly shaped joint.

This control system was the first of its kind; it was developed in 1983.

How could human reactions alone control something as fast as a rocket in flight? The need for instant access to information was vital. This need was met by the high-speed calculators called computers. And the need for speedy, accurate, non-human performance was met by totally automated machines called robots. Computers and robots working together seem to have unlimited capacity for getting things done rapidly and efficiently. It is not surprising, then, that a race toward total automation has developed between the United States, Japan, and West Germany. The prize is industrial supremacy. Largely responsible for this forward leap of automation is the great progress made in computer science.

Computers are being used to control most

automated industrial systems. Petroleum refineries, for example, are being run almost completely by computer. The few workers needed to operate the plant spend most of their time in a control room watching dials and other indicators. The computer sends and receives signals to and from various machine parts. It turns valves on and off automatically and detects and reports possible trouble spots. The memory of the computer has been programmed to do all this.

Many other large plants are operated in this way—textile mills, steel mills, automobile and aircraft plants. Advanced computer systems control the equipment of the banking industry and many large businesses. And, because computers can perform at rates that may be as high as millions of operations per second, their use with the equipment of scientific and technological laboratories is invaluable. Automated libraries quickly provide such research facilities with essential information. *See also* ROBOTICS. H.S.B./G.D.B.

# AUTOMOBILE

An automobile (ȯt′ ə mō bēl′), or car, is a four-wheeled, self-propelled passenger vehicle. A gasoline, diesel, or electric engine provides the force that moves an automobile. Small automobiles carry two people, the driver and the passenger. Larger autos can carry up to ten people. Automobiles are produced in large, automated factories that build many vehicles each day. The largest automobile plants in the United States are near Detroit, Michigan.

**History**   In 1769, Nicolas Cugnot of France used a steam engine to propel a crude wheeled vehicle. The first practical internal combustion engine was built by a French inventor, Etienne Lenoir, about 1860. A German engineer, Nikolaus Otto, built a more effi-

cient gas engine in 1876. In 1885, Karl Benz and Gottlieb Daimler, of Germany, used Otto's engine on four-wheeled carriages to make the first true automobiles. Early models were built by hand and were expensive. In 1913, Henry Ford, an American, introduced the conveyor belt to carry automobile parts on assembly lines. This made it possible to produce many automobiles in a short time. Ford was able to lower prices so that many more people could afford automobiles. Other manufacturers did the same.

There were several major United States automobile manufacturers in the 1920s. Of them, only three are still in business: Ford Motor Company, General Motors, and Chrysler. American Motors, the other large American automobile maker, started doing business in the late 1950s.

After World War II, Volkswagen, a German company, began to sell many of its small cars in the United States. They were called "Beetles." Today, cars produced in Germany and Japan account for a very large number of all automobile sales in the United States. American manufacturers are able to produce more than 8 million automobiles in a year. They bring out new models each year.

**Assembly**   An automobile body is attached to the structure of steel beams called a chassis. The chassis is very strong. It absorbs many strains and stresses. They body consists of thin sheet metal with some structural steel beams built in for added strength. Some bodies are made of aluminum or fiberglass.

Automobiles are built on assembly lines. Groups of workers install different parts as the uncompleted automobiles are moved past them. Major units, such as engines and transmissions, are assembled on their own assembly lines. When completed, they are brought to the main assembly line and put into the automobile at the proper time. Computers are used to keep track of all the hundreds of parts that go into each car. Completed automobiles are rolled off the end of the assembly line, tested, and delivered to dealers by trains and large trucks.

**Engines** The gasoline engine is used as the power source in most automobiles. Some autos are powered by diesel engines. Diesel engines are heavier and more expensive than gasoline engines. They traditionally last longer than gasoline engines, however. Rotary engines, developed from the German Wankel engine, are used in some small cars. Electric engines that run on stored electricity in batteries have been developed for small cars to be used for city driving. They are not in wide use. Some manufacturers have experimented with gas turbine engines for automobiles. But they have been found to be too expensive to produce in quantity.

Most automobile engines have four, six, or eight cylinders. Gasoline is mixed with air and compressed inside each cylinder. It is ignited with a spark from a sparkplug. The explosion forces a piston to move downwards. An arm attached to the piston turns a large shaft at the bottom of the engine called the crankshaft. The crankshaft turns gears in the transmission. Those gears turn a driveshaft that supplies power to the wheels. (*See* ENGINE.)

Most engines are mounted in the front end of the automobile. An engine can drive the rear wheels. Front-mounted engines drive the front wheels in most new automobiles. Engines can also be mounted in the rear of the car and drive the rear wheels.

An automobile engine needs electricity to ignite the gas-air mixture in its cylinders. It generates its own electricity with a generator or alternator. Some of the electricity is stored in a lead-acid battery. Every car has a battery. Electricity from the battery is used to start the

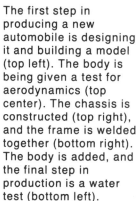

The first step in producing a new automobile is designing it and building a model (top left). The body is being given a test for aerodynamics (top center). The chassis is constructed (top right), and the frame is welded together (bottom right). The body is added, and the final step in production is a water test (bottom left).

engine and to operate lights and accessories.

Engines create a great amount of heat when they are running. The explosions in the cylinders have a temperature of 1,927°C [3,500°F]. Cylinder temperatures must be brought down to about 71°C [160°F] in order to prevent damage to the engine. Cool air is blown across the engine by a fan attached to the front end. In some engines, a cooling system circulates a mixture of water and chemicals around the cylinder walls to cool them. The water-chemical mixture gets hot in the process. It is cooled again by running it through the radiator mounted in front of the engine. Other engines are air cooled.

Lubrication systems circulate oil throughout the engine to reduce friction between moving parts. Exhaust systems remove waste gases that result from combustion in the cylinders. Mufflers reduce the noise caused by this combustion.

**Transmission**   Engine power is transmitted to the wheels through the clutch, transmission, drive shaft, and differential. These parts are called the drive train. The clutch links the power in the crankshaft with the drive train. The clutch can be mechanical or hydraulic. Mechanical clutches are operated by a foot pedal. Hydraulic clutches operate automatically by fluid pressure. The transmission contains gears of different sizes. Manual transmissions require the driver to change gears by moving the gearshift lever. Automatic transmissions do away with clutch pedals and gearshift levers. Gears are shifted automatically by means of hydraulic pressure. Cars start forward slowly in low gear. Second gear picks up speed. High gear maintains driving, or cruising, speed. Some small cars have four or five sets of forward gears.

The drive shaft carries the power from the transmission to the differential. The differential is a set of gears that drives the wheels. When an automobile goes around a corner, the outside wheel must turn faster since it has

These two classic automobiles exemplify milestones in the history of the automotive industry. The wagonlike machine at the top is a Daimler of 1886. The other machine is an Austin 7 racer of 1922.

a greater distance to travel than the inside wheel. The differential is designed to allow the wheels to turn at different speeds.

**Steering, braking, suspension**   The driver uses the steering wheel to guide the car. The steering wheel turns the steering column. The steering column is linked to the front wheels by a steering box that contains a set of gears. The gears make it easier for the driver to turn the heavy front wheels. Some cars are equipped with power steering. This allows hydraulic pressure to aid the driver.

Automobiles are required by law to have dual braking systems for safety. The main braking system, operated by a foot pedal, acts on all four wheels. It is a hydraulic system. When the driver steps on the brake, fluid is pumped from a master cylinder to each wheel. The fluid forces two small pistons outward against the brake drum, or discs, which are attached to the wheels. A second braking system, called the parking brake, is operated by a hand lever. The lever is connected to wires that pull the brake drums against the rear wheels only. The parking brake will hold a parked car on a hill. It does not have the strength to stop a fast moving car. Automatic transmissions can be set in positions that lock the gears and prevent the drive wheels from turning. This will keep a car from moving if it is parked on a hill.

The suspension system consists of heavy coil and leaf springs and shock absorbers. It helps to make the ride more comfortable by cushioning the car when it goes over bumps.

**Automobile safety**   Traffic accidents in the United States during recent years have resulted in an average of 50,000 deaths and millions of injuries each year. Many accidents are caused by drivers who drive too fast. The national speed limit of 89 kph [55 mph] that was put into effect in 1974 has been credited with saving many lives. Many of the accidents are caused by drivers who are driving under the influence of alcohol or drugs.

Manufacturers who sell new cars in the United States are required to equip those cars with safety devices like seat belts, shoulder harnesses, and shatterproof windows. Collapsible steering columns and high-impact bumpers are also required. Only about 20% of all United States drivers use the seat belts and shoulder harnesses in their cars. Safety experts say that over 10,000 lives could be saved each year if all drivers used the belts and harnesses.

Automobiles have become safer and more efficient over the years. Today's tires adhere to road surfaces better and are manufactured to help give better gas mileage. They also last longer. Improved suspensions and braking systems enable automobiles to handle better than ever. Automobile manufacturers have added steel supports to vital areas of the body. The supports help the bodies to withstand impacts with greater safety. Smaller, more fuel-efficient engines have replaced larger ones without sacrificing too much power.

The National Highway Traffic Safety Administration (NHTSA) sets the safety standards for new automobiles. It sometimes orders manufacturers to recall cars that have been found to have safety defects. A car that has been recalled must be repaired by the manufacturer at no charge to the owner.

W.R.P./R.W.L.

**AVALANCHE** (av' ə lanch') An avalanche is a mass of snow, ice, rock debris, or soil, that suddenly starts to slide or fall down a mountain slope. Spring rains, dry warm winds, and vibrations caused by loud noises and earthquakes can start an avalanche.

To prevent the loss of life to skiers and mountain climbers, Switzerland pioneered devices for testing areas for avalanches. In the United States, avalanches are watched for by the Forest Service of the Department of Agriculture.

The largest avalanche in North America took place in the Cascade Mountains of Canada in 1965. It is called the Hope Slide. 127,092,000 metric tons [140,000,000 tons] of rock and mud fell 1,200 m [3,900 ft] to cover part of the British Columbian highway. It buried three moving cars. The Hope Slide was as wide as 3 km [2 mi] and as deep as 90 m [300 ft].

S.A.B./W.R.S.

# AVIATION, HISTORY OF

Aviation (ā' vē ā' shən) is the science of designing, developing, building, and flying aircraft. As long ago as the 1500s, the Italian Leonardo da Vinci designed wings that would flap for a man to use in flight. However, as far as we know, he never built a full-size model of them for use. He also designed helicopters and parachutes. The Montgolfier brothers, of France, were the first human beings on record to fly. Their first flight, in 1783, was in a hot-air balloon.

In the early 1800s, Sir George Cayley, an English scientist, developed and flew the first glider. He was the first person to recognize that fixed, curved wings are better than flapping wings for heavier-than-air craft. Cayley became known as "The Father of Aviation." At about the same time, a Frenchman, Henri Giffard, built a cigar-shaped balloon capable of carrying a man. It was filled with hydrogen gas and powered by a steam engine that turned a propeller. In the 1800s, Otto Lilienthal, of Germany, and Octave Chanute and Samuel Langley, of the United States, improved upon gliders.

In 1903 two American brothers, Wilbur and Orville Wright, built an aircraft powered by a home-built gasoline engine that drove a propeller. On December 17, 1903, Orville Wright made the first successful powered flight at Kittyhawk, North Carolina. The airplane was named *Flyer*. It stayed in the air for 12 seconds.

In 1909, a Frenchman, Louis Blériot, flew a plane of his own design from France to England, across the English Channel. Lighter-than-air craft were still being developed at that time. Count Ferdinand von Zeppelin, of Germany, built a huge, metal-framed airship called a dirigible. The cigar-shaped balloon was filled with hydrogen. The dirigible carried passengers and was powered by several engines. The name "Zeppelin" became synonymous with dirigible.

World War I (1914–1918) brought about many new developments in aviation. Dirigibles were used for observation and for bombing missions. Planes of all shapes and sizes were built for military use even though they were not thought of as major weapons at that

time. Most designs featured two wings, one placed over the other. They were called biplanes. Triplanes had three wings. With the introduction of metal construction, single-wing planes, or monoplanes, started to come into use toward the end of World War I. Fighter planes and scout planes had one engine. Machine guns were mounted on most planes. They were timed to fire through the spinning propeller without hitting it. Aerial fights between planes became known as "dogfights." Larger planes, called bombers, had two or three engines.

In 1919, the first commercial airline was started. Air Transport and Travel, Ltd. carried passengers throughout England in modified DeHavilland bombers.

In May 1919, a team of United States Navy pilots made the first flight across the Atlantic Ocean in a Curtiss NC-4 flying boat. They flew from the United States to England. A month later, two Englishmen, John Alcock and Arthur Brown, flew a Vickers Vimy aircraft from England to the United States.

In the 1920s, air mail routes were started in the United States. "Barnstorming" pilots toured the country in their planes, introducing aviation to small towns and cities. They put on flying shows and took people for plane rides. In 1923, Juan del la Cierva, of Spain, designed and flew the first autogyro. It was a forerunner to the helicopter. In 1926, Commander Richard Byrd, of the United States, flew an airplane over the North Pole. In 1927, Charles Lindbergh became one of America's heroes when he flew his plane, the *Spirit of St. Louis,* non-stop from New York to Paris in 33½ hours. In 1929, *Graf Zeppelin,* a German dirigible, flew 34,298 km [21,500 mi] around the world in just three weeks. The *Graf Zeppelin* was 236.3 m [775 ft] long.

The air transport industry began to grow in the early 1930s. In the United States, the Ford Trimotor, a passenger plane with three engines, was used by most airlines. Many cities built airports. Airline routes were ex-

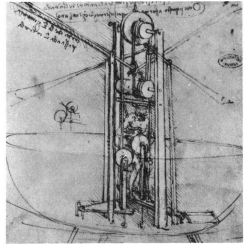

Milestones in the history of aviation.
1. Design for an early flying machine by
Leonardo da Vinci. 2. The hot air balloon
of the Montgolfier brothers, 1783. 3. The
glider of George Cayley, 1804. 4. Otto
Lilienthal, a German pioneer of gliding,
with his 1895 glider. 5. The first
powered flight, made on December 17, 1903
by the Wright brothers in the United States.
6. The first European flight, made in
1906 by Alberto Santos-Dumont. His plane
had a pusher propeller.

tended to more and more locations. The Boeing Aircraft Company built the first all-metal passenger plane in 1933. It was a monoplane and had landing gear that could be folded up into the body of the plane during flight. It also had de-icing equipment that allowed it to fly at high altitudes and in bad weather. The de-icers kept ice from forming on the wings. The Boeing DC-3 transport plane was developed from this model. Thousands of DC-3s were built by Boeing between 1935 and 1945. They were durable and dependable and became a familiar sight in the sky. DC-3s were the most

used transport planes in the 1940s, especially during World War II, when they were referred to as C-47's. Some DC-3s built in the late 1940s are still flying.

In May, 1937, the German dirigible *Hindenburg,* which used hydrogen gas, exploded during a landing at Lakehurst, New Jersey, after a flight across the Atlantic. Many passengers were killed. Dirigible flights were stopped soon after and never resumed. Hot air balloons owned by individuals and advertising blimps are the only lighter-than-air craft in use today. Blimps are similar to dirigibles in shape. They are like balloons in that they do not have interior framework and use helium, a

7. Louis Blériot in his monoplane, in which he flew the English Channel in 1909. 8. The S.E.5a British fighter plane of the First World War. This plane was built of a wooden frame covered with fabric. Its top speed was 120 mph, its maximum altitude 20,000 feet. 9. The German airship Graf Zeppelin, which in 1929 made a three-week 21,500 mile trip around the world. 10. The American P-51 Mustang fighter of 1942, with a top speed of 465 mph. 11. The German Heinkel 178, first turbojet aircraft. 12. The Russian MiG-21 speedy combat plane.

gas that does not burn. Blimps are much smaller than dirigibles.

World War II brought many new developments in aviation. The airplane became a major weapon of war for the first time. Bombers were used against enemy targets. Fighter planes were able to attack fairly close to the ground as well as in the air. ''Air power,'' as it was called, played a large part in the Allies' victory over Germany and Japan.

Aircraft manufacturers expanded their plants in order to meet military needs. Assembly lines were set up so that large numbers of planes could be built quickly. In the United States, 50,000 planes a year were built. New materials were used that improved the quality of airplanes. Larger and more powerful engines let planes fly faster and higher. Fighter planes flew at 480 to 640 kph [300 to 400 mph]. Jet engines were developed toward the end of the war but did not come into wide use until after 1945.

**Aviation today** The air transport industry has continued to grow. There are now thousands of airports in the United States. Many jet airliners fly at about 960 kph (600 mph), and they carry more than 200 million passengers each year. Special electronic equipment allows planes to be flown safely in almost any kind of weather.

Boeing 747 "jumbo jets" can carry up to 500 passengers. The 747s also carry cargo. The *Concorde*, a passenger airliner, developed by the British and the French, can fly about 2,400 kph (1,500 mph). It has cut flying time between Europe and the United States to about three hours.

Many business firms whose executives travel a great deal found that they could save money by owning their own planes. Many of these fly as fast as commercial airliners and have navigation instruments similar to those of larger planes.

Throughout the history of aviation, interest in recreational flying has always been high. Many people own their own planes just for the thrill of being able to fly. Usually these privately owned planes are small, propeller-driven craft that can carry two to four people. By the early 1980s, a new kind of recreational airplane was popular. These are the "ultralights," glider-like planes with wings, a seat or harness to hold the pilot, and a small engine.

Perhaps the most important advance in aviation since the jet engine was the successful testing of the space shuttle *Columbia*. The space shuttle is the first reusable spacecraft. It is launched like a rocket but lands like an airplane. Between April 1981 and November 1984, fourteen flights were made. The first four were made to find out how well the space shuttle would work. On later flights, communications satellites were repaired in space and new ones launched. Eventually, the space shuttle will have many uses, including carrying people from one space station to another.

In the mid-1970s when the cost of oil rose sharply, commercial and cargo transport airlines were seriously affected. Higher fuel costs meant that unless the large airplanes flew at full capacity all the time, they would not be profitable.

Most of the major airlines and manufac-

The Gates Learjet (above) is the most popular business jet in the world. The upturned wingtips reduce drag and increase forward power. The space shuttle *Columbia* (right) is shown lifting off on the first operational flight of the shuttle system.

turers seemed to agree on the need for a fuel-efficient transport that would carry 150 to 200 passengers. The first of these, the Boeing 757 and 767, were operating in mid-1982.

Along with the use of computers in navigation systems, expanded use of cathode ray tube (CRT) displays in cockpit areas has continued. CRT displays allow airplane personnel to get flight information easily and quickly.

The United States government regulates aviation through the Federal Aviation Administration (FAA). The FAA is responsible for overseeing safety and progress in aviation. *See also* AERODYNAMICS; AIRPLANE.

W.R.P./J.VP.

**AVOCADO** (av′ ə käd′ ō) An avocado is a fruit grown from a tree of the same name. The tree belongs to the family Lauraceae. It was originally found in tropical South America. The avocado is now planted in warm regions around the world. The fruit is pear-shaped with a green, thick skin. The flesh is yel-

Recent models of commercial jet aircraft, such as the 767 pictured above, were designed to be more efficient than previous models.

lowish and coarse. It is eaten with salads. The fruit is also called an alligator pear.

S.R.G./F.W.S.

Avocets are long-legged wading birds. The upward curving bill of this bird is a special adaptation for feeding under water.

**AVOCET** (av′ ə set′) An avocet is a wading bird that belongs to the family Recurvirostridae. There are four species of avocets. One is found in North America. The others are found in South America, Australia, and

Eurasia. The avocet lives along the shoreline. It feeds by wading in shallow water and swinging its curved beak through the water. It eats small insects and crustaceans. S.R.G./L.S.

## AVOGADRO, AMEDEO (1776–1856)

Amedeo Avogadro (ä′ vō gä′ drō) was an Italian physicist who made several important discoveries about molecules. In 1811, he stated that equal volumes of any gases at the same temperature and pressure contain the same number of molecules. This statement, known as Avogadro's law, is a principle used in a method of finding atomic weights.

A mole is the molecular weight of a substance stated in grams. One mole of any substance contains $6.023 \times 10^{23}$ molecules. This number is called Avogadro's constant or Avogadro's number. Avogadro was the first person to tell the difference between an atom and a molecule. This difference was necessary to obtain correct values for atomic weights and molecular weights. Not until after Avogadro's death was his work accepted and praised. J.J.A./D.G.F.

## AXIL

**AXIL** (ak′ səl) The axil is the angle between the upper part of a leaf or leaf stem and the branch from which it is growing. The axil is located just above the node. Branches, flowers, leaves, or thorns grow from buds which form at the nodes. In some plants, such as the lily, the axil may produce buds which can be used to grow a new plant. *See also* PLANT KINGDOM. A.J.C./M.H.S.

## AZIMUTH

**AZIMUTH** (az′ məth) Azimuth is the position or bearing of an object on earth or in the sky in relation to a fixed point, usually north. Azimuth is measured as an angle of 0° to 360°.

In navigation, the stars are used to figure out an azimuth. This lets sailors know where they are in the ocean. Surveyors and mapmakers also use azimuths. A.J.C./C.R.

## BABBAGE, CHARLES (1792–1871)

Charles Babbage (bab′ ij) was an English mathematician whose work led to the development of the modern automatic computer. He was the first to experiment with memory banks and punched cards for his computers. Although most of his work was with calculators, Babbage established many of the principles used in even the most complex of today's computers.

Babbage also invented the speedometer and the locomotive cowcatcher. *See also* CALCULATING MACHINE. A.J.C./D.G.F.

## BABOON

**BABOON** (ba bün′) A baboon is a large monkey found in the rocky regions, open woodlands, and plains of Africa and Arabia. The baboon has a large head and long, sharp teeth. A baboon's arms are about the same length as its legs. A male baboon is much larger than a female baboon.

Baboons can carry food in pouches that are inside their cheeks. They feed on vegetables, fruit, grass, insects, leaves, and roots. Baboons are social animals, living in groups of from ten to a hundred. A large male usually rules. Male baboons, regarded as tough fighters, have been known to attack leopards.

The male hamadryas baboon of Ethiopia, Arabia, Egypt, the Sudan, and Somaliland, has long, gray hair on its head and shoulders. The people of Egypt once thought this animal was sacred. The chacma baboon of South Africa has grayish brown hair on its body, and a long collar of hair, or ruff, around its neck. This baboon often damages crops.

J.J.A./J.J.M.

## BABYLONIAN CIVILIZATION

**BABYLONIAN CIVILIZATION** One of the greatest of the ancient civilizations developed about 4,000 years ago around a city

called Babylon, the capital of the empire of Babylonia (bab′ ə lō′ nē ə). The 1,500 years of Babylonian civilization that followed, 2000 to 500 B.C., produced important advances in astronomy, mathematics, architecture, engineering, writing, and law. Between 600 and 500 B.C., Babylon became the largest city in the world. It was a major center of science, art, commerce, and religion.

The root of the progress made by the people of Babylonian civilization was cuneiform writing, a system of characters, like letters, that organized communication. The wedge-shaped characters of cuneiform writing were placed at various angles and in groups of 2 to 30. This system of symbols permitted the Babylonians to maintain libraries, write books, record history, and promote education. The Babylonians created a vast literature. Some of the myths of Babylonia are very similar to some parts of the Bible, like the creation of the earth and the great flood. About 1750 B.C., Babylonian civilization produced what was probably the world's first written code of law. Called the Code of Hammurabi, it was named after a king of Babylonia. Archeologists examining the ruins of Babylon found the code inscribed on a column of the king's palace. They also found more than 150,000 clay tablets inscribed with cuneiform writing.

In astronomy and mathematics, the Babylonians had great success. Their records show that they divided a circle into 360 degrees and an hour into 60 minutes. Also, as their records show, they had knowledge of fractions, square roots, and squares. The Babylonians were able to predict eclipses of the moon. They recorded their observations of the sky, also advancing astrology.

Because their capital city was spread out on both sides of a river and their economic life was based on agriculture, the Babylonians learned how to build bridges, aqueducts, and irrigation canals. Their engineering skills involved maps and surveys that required leveling instruments and measuring rods. The Babylonians constructed sanitary and drainage systems. They even had a kind of farmer's almanac to improve their agriculture.

Babylonian builders were responsible for the construction of two of the most marvelous buildings of ancient times. The ziggurat, a seven-story temple-tower of baked brick, is linked by legend with the biblical Tower of Babel. Under their greatest king, Nebuchadnezzar II, the Babylonians built the Hanging Gardens, which the ancient Greeks called one of the Seven Wonders of the World. Within Babylon were many splendid structures, especially the palaces of the kings and the temples of the gods.

During the 1,500 years of its existence, Babylon was destroyed and rebuilt several times. At one time, the rulers of Babylonia were conquered by invaders. At another time, the rulers of Babylonia conquered other kingdoms and took captives. The Babylonian empire came to an end when Babylon was conquered by the Persians under Cyrus the Great in 539 B.C.

Until the nineteenth century, scholars and scientists depended on writings from ancient Greece for their information on Babylonian civilization. During the past 100 years, archeologists and other scientists have greatly increased our knowledge of Babylonian civilization. Examples of Babylonian science and art are found in several of the leading museums of Europe and the United States. *See also* ARCHEOLOGY.                G.M.B./S.O.

**BACKSWIMMER** (bak′ swim ər) The backswimmers are also called boat bugs. They are one of many types of water bugs. Although backswimmers spend most of their lives in the water, they are able to fly long distances. These insects are small, usually 3 to 17 mm [0.118 to 0.669 in] in length. They

Left, this portrait of an olive baboon shows the long muzzle characteristic of the species.

use their long, flat hind legs to paddle through the water. They usually swim on their backs. Their short front legs are used for holding prey. ackswimmers hold a bubble of air between their wings and body. They use the air in the bubble for breathing when they are underwater. This lets them stay underwater for as long as six hours. Backswimmers spend the winter buried in the mud at the bottom of a pond or stream.

Backswimmers have sharp beaks which they use for stabbing fish and other small water animals. They suck the juices out of their victims. Backswimmers can also give painful bites to people.          A.J.C./J.R.

Backswimmers use their long rear legs as oars.

**BACON, FRANCIS** (1561–1626) Francis Bacon (bā′ kən) was an English philosopher and statesman who developed a scientific method for solving problems. Bacon felt that people should have control over the world around them. The way to get this control is through knowledge. The way to get knowledge is through science.

Bacon stated that there are several things which keep people from getting knowledge. First, people tend to decide something is generally true if they have found it to be true in only one or two cases. They do not test it to find out if it is true in all cases. Second, people base decisions on their own backgrounds and educations. They do not consider that someone with a different background and education might make a different decision. Third, people have to use words to describe something. Since words can be confusing, it is important to be exact in a description. Bacon called these blocks of knowledge prejudices.

Once these prejudices are put aside, people can obtain knowledge through inductive reasoning. Inductive reasoning involves making many observations and tests before arriving at any conclusions. Bacon suggested that lists be prepared. One list is for things that are true. A second list is for things that are not true. A third list is for things that are more true than not. For example, a person has seen only red apples. He says, "All apples are red." He believes this until he sees a yellow apple. He may then say, "Most apples are red." If he had made lists as suggested by Bacon, he would find that there are many red apples and many yellow apples. It would be better for him to say, "There are red apples and yellow apples." Bacon's theory states that the more often an idea is tested and found to be true, the more likely it is to be true.

Since Bacon was highly respected as a philosopher, his views were widely accepted. His work helped greatly in the progress of Renaissance science. *See also* INDUCTION (LOGICAL).          A.J.C./D.G.F.

**BACTERIA** (bak tir′ ē ə) Bacteria (singular, bacterium) are one-celled organisms. They are among the smallest and most widespread of all living things. They may live alone or in groups called colonies. Bacteria belong to the kingdom Monera. Bacteria, or something like them, were probably the first living organisms on earth. (*See* EVOLUTION.) They reproduce so quickly that one bacterium can produce millions of others in only a few hours.

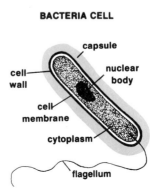

**BACTERIA CELL**

capsule
nuclear body
cell wall
cell membrane
cytoplasm
flagellum

Diagram of a bacterium. This one-celled organism gets everything it needs for life directly from its environment. The single flagellum provides locomotion. Bacteria are classified as plants.

**FOUR TYPES OF BACTERIA**

spirilla are
spiral shaped

Vibrios are
shaped like bent cigars

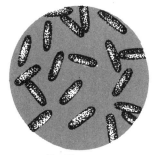
Bacilli are
rod shaped

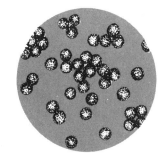
Cocci are round
and usually exist in colonies

Bacteria are classified according to their shape. Once the shape of a disease-causing agent has been established, specific tests can be run to identify it.

**Structure and life of bacteria** Most bacterial cells have a strong cell wall, as do plants. Many bacteria have a capsule, a coating surrounding the cell wall. Some bacteria are able to move only by floating passively in the air or water. Most others, though, can move under their own power. Some wriggle from one place to another, while others use a whiplike flagellum to swim. (*See* FLAGELLUM.)

Bacteria have one of four shapes. Since they are so small, their shapes can only be seen with a microscope. The coccus (plural, cocci) is round. The bacillus (plural, bacilli) is rod-shaped. The vibrio (plural, vibrios) is shaped like a bent cigar. The spirillum (plural, spirilla) is spiral-shaped.

Bacteria usually reproduce by fission. (*See* ASEXUAL REPRODUCTION.) In fission, the organism splits into two new organisms. It is by rapid fission that bacteria are able to reproduce in such great numbers. At times, bacteria may exchange DNA and other genetic material in a type of sexual reproduction. Some bacteria produce endospores for reproduction. (*See* ENDOSPORE.) These endospores are very strong. They are often able to survive for extended periods of time in unfavorable conditions.

Bacteria may live in soil, in water, in air, or in another organisms. Although most bacteria live at temperatures between 10 to 40°C [50 to 104°F], some require either very hot or very cold temperatures in order to grow and reproduce. Some bacteria are aerobic, and require air to live. (*See* AEROBE.) Other bacteria are anaerobic, and do not require air to live. (*See* ANAEROBE.) Often, anaerobic bacteria die if they are exposed to air.

Some bacteria produce their own food by photosynthesis. (*See* PHOTOSYNTHESIS.) Others use chemicals as food. Some bacteria are parasites and rely on other living organisms called hosts for food. Some of these parasites harm their hosts while others live symbiotically. (*See* SYMBIOSIS.) Some bacteria are saprophytes and get their food from dead organisms. These saprophytic bacteria are important parts of the food chain and other cycles involving carbon, nitrogen, oxygen, and sulfur. Underground oil and natural gas deposits may be the result of the work done by saprophytic bacteria millions of years ago.

A bacteriologist uses a microscope to examine bacteria that have been grown in agar jelly.

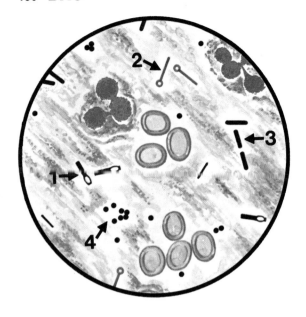

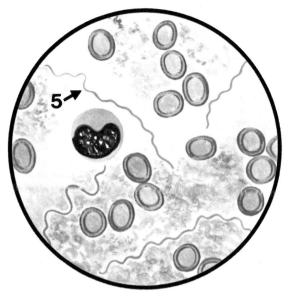

Two microscopic views of human blood smears stained to show harmful bacteria. These bacteria are numbered. **1** is *Clostridium tetani*, the cause of tetanus, or lockjaw. **2** and **3** are other types of Clostridia. Notice that **1** and **2** have endospores, seen as rounded swellings, whereas **3** does not. **4** indicates a group of staphylococci. Staphylococci can cause boils and blood poisoning. The blood smear on the right was taken from a person suffering from relapsing fever. The number **5** points to *Borellia recurrentis*, the microorganism that causes relapsing fever. Microscopic examination is just one of the steps taken in the identification of disease-causing organisms.

**Helpful bacteria**   Most bacteria are useful. Certain bacteria are needed to make cheese, yogurt, and butter. Some bacteria are used in the treatment of sewage and garbage. These bacteria release methane gas as they digest the wastes. (There are cities in the United States and in Europe that use these bacteria as the source of their entire energy supply.) One newly discovered type of bacteria can be used to clean up oil spills in the oceans. Still other bacteria live in the human body. These bacteria help with digestion and help the body to produce vitamins. (*See* DIGESTION.) Some bacteria actually aid in the prevention of infections.

**Harmful bacteria**   Some bacteria can cause food spoilage in improperly processed foods. This may result in botulism or other forms of food poisoning. (*See* FOOD POISONING.) Some bacteria are pathogenic, or disease-causing. Some cause diseases in plants which can destroy entire fields of crops. Some bacteria cause sicknesses in animals, including human beings. Some of the human diseases caused by bacteria are tuberculosis, tetanus, leprosy, syphilis, and gonorrhea. Some bacterial diseases can be fought successfully by the body's own defenses. (*See* ANTIBODY.) Vaccinations can help the body build up certain antibodies to prevent a sickness or to make it less severe. (*See* IMMUNITY.) Certain drugs attack only bacteria. (*See* ANTIBIOTIC.) The use of antibiotics and sulfa drugs has done much to help control the spread and danger of bacterial diseases and epidemics. *See also* BACTERIOPHAGE; DISEASE; KOCH, ROBERT; PASTEUR, LOUIS.                        A.J.C./E.R.L.

**BACTERIOPHAGE** (bak tir′ ē ə fāj′) A bacteriophage is any virus that attacks bacteria. The word bacteriophage means "bacteria eater." A bacteriophage, like all viruses, is acellular—that is, not a cell. It is made of protein.

Bacteriophages are of many different shapes and sizes. Some bacteriophages have hollow, rod-shaped "tails" and sphere or T-shaped "heads." Others are threadlike.

The heads contain nucleic acids. (*See* NUC-LEIC ACID.) The infection of a bacterial cell by a tailed virus involves attachment of the bacteriophage tail to the cell wall of a bacterium. (*See* BACTERIA.) Then the nucleic acid is injected through the tail into the bacterium. The genetic information in this nucleic acid causes other bacteriophages to be formed inside the bacterium. If the bacterium dies, the new bacteriophages are released and attack other bacteria. Bacteriophages that do not kill the host bacterium may help it to become resistant to certain drugs. (*See* ANTIBIOTIC.) Scientists often use bacteriophages to help them understand heredity. *See also* DNA; HEREDITY; MOLECULAR BIOLOGY. A.J.C./E.R.L.

A badger on the prowl. Badgers are burrowing animals. They usually come out of their holes only at night.

**BADGER** (baj′ ər) The badger is a mammal that is a member of the family Mustelidae. (*See* MAMMAL.) The Mustelid family also includes the weasel, skunk, and otter. The badger is found in the prairies and plains of the western United States and Canada. It lives in holes that it digs in the ground. A badger is a heavy-set animal with short legs, short ears, and a doglike head. It grows to lengths of 60 cm [2 ft]. The fur of the badger is silvery gray with black and white markings on the head. Badgers are omnivorous, eating many different things. (*See* OMNIVORE.) Much of its food is small mammals such as mice, which it hunts at night. The badger is not very fast, but fights fiercely when attacked. The fur of the badger is used to make paint brushes, shaving brushes, and coat trimmings. S.R.G./J.J.M.

**BAEKELAND, LEO** (1863–1944) Leo Baekeland (bāk′ land) was an American chemist known for the invention of Bakelite, an early plastic. Baekeland was born in Ghent, Belgium. He moved to the United States in 1889.

In 1891, Baekeland invented a sensitive photographic paper. Eastman-Kodak bought it from him for one million dollars. Baekeland then tried to invent a synthetic substitute for shellac. He experimented with resins made by reacting phenol and formaldehyde. In 1909, he produced a resin that was resistant to water and solvents, was an electric insulator, and was easy to shape and cut. The substance Bakelite, named after him, was the first synthetic resin as well as the first thermosetting plastic. J.J.A./D.G.F.

**BAER, KARL ERNST VON** (1792–1876) Karl Ernst von Baer (bār) was a German biologist who pioneered the field of embryology. Embryology is the study of the development of embryos, organisms in the earlier stages of development. Baer worked with the eggs of female mammals. He identified the mammal egg as being the same as the eggs of other animals. He wrote two important books, *The Origin of Mammal Eggs,* and *The Embryology of Animals.* P.G.C./D.G.F.

**BAKELITE** (bā′ kə līt′) Bakelite, called phenolic resin by chemists, is a plastic made from phenol and formaldehyde. This was the first truly synthetic plastic. It was put into commercial use by 1916. It is a thermosetting plastic, one which sets when heated and cannot be molded. Bakelite is dark in color. It is widely used because it resists heat and is comparatively cheap to produce.

Bakelite was once used for the handles of kettles, pans, and irons. It is also a good electric insulator. It is used in the electrical industry and in the home for light switches, holders, plugs, and other fittings. Another use of Bakelite is in laminations with wood, fabric, and other materials to make tough, heat-proof substances. The invention of Bakelite opened the door to modern plastics.

J.J.A./J.M.

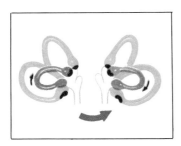

The semicircular canals of the inner ear control the body's balance. Any movement (red arrow) of the body causes a liquid in the canals to move (black arrows). The moving liquid affects sensitive hair cells, which set up nerve impulses to the brain. The brain then instructs various muscles to move to preserve the balance of the body.

**BALANCE** (bal′ əns) A balance is an accurate device used to measure the weight of chemicals and other substances in a laboratory. It consists of a horizontal bar balanced on a thin edge of metal. A pointer attached to the bar moves when the bar is tilted in either direction. Small pans are suspended from each end of the bar. The substance to be weighed is placed in one pan. Numbered weights of different sizes are placed in the other pan. When the weight in both pans is equal, the bar is horizontal and the pointer is motionless. The weight of the substance is found by adding up the weights needed to balance the pans.

Laboratory balances are delicate instruments. They are kept in glass cases to protect them against moisture and gases in the air. Balances must be adjusted for temperature and moisture before each use. Electric balances and electric microbalances are used for even more accurate measurements. *See also* SCALE; WEIGHT.　　　　W.R.P./R.W.L.

Gibbons, like human beings, depend for balance on structures in the inner ear.

**BALD EAGLE** (bȯld ē′ gəl) The bald eagle or white headed eagle (*Haliaetus leucocephalus*) is a large, North American bird of prey. It is the national bird of the United States. The adult bald eagle reaches a length of 75 to 90 cm [30 to 35 in], a wingspread of 2 m [6.6 ft], and a weight of 3.5 to 6.5 kg [7.7 to 14.3 lb]. Bald eagles may live as long as 30 years. They have very sharp eyes and can spot prey from great heights.

The bald eagle is brown and has white feathers on its head and tail. These white head feathers are what make the eagle look bald.

The bald eagle is rare. Though it was once found throughout North America, most of the 2,400 remaining birds are in Alaska. Because bald eagles usually eat fish and small animals, Alaskan hunters killed more than 100,000 bald eagles between 1917 and 1952 in an attempt to protect the salmon and fur industries. The bald eagle is now protected by federal law.

Currently, a major threat to bald eagles is pesticides. These chemicals concentrate in the bird's body causing it to lay infertile or weak-shelled eggs or deformed young.

The bald eagle has long stood for freedom and strength. It is a part of the American Indian heritage.                    A.J.C./L.S.

The bald eagle is the national emblem of the United States. It is in danger of extinction and so is protected.

**BALLISTICS** (bə lis′ tiks) Ballistics is the science concerned with the motion and behavior of projectiles, such as bullets, bombs, rockets, and guided missiles. The three main branches of ballistics are interior, exterior, and terminal ballistics.

Interior ballistics deals with the motion of a projectile as it travels down the barrel of a weapon, such as a rifle or pistol. The weight of the bullet, the pressure placed on the bullet, the speed at which the bullet moves through the barrel, the barrel's length and diameter, and the speed at which the bullet leaves the barrel all affect the flight of the bullet. A person who studies the interior ballistics of a rifle or pistol has to know all these things. The interior ballistics of missiles is concerned with the design of rocket engines and the choice of propellants. A rocket is propelled by the reaction to expanding gases escaping from it.

The speed at which a projectile leaves a gun barrel or a missile leaves a launch is called the initial velocity. The initial velocity of the projectiles of some rifles is 1,500 m [5,000 ft] per second. The initial velocity of missiles is lower because most missiles are much heavier than a bullet.

Exterior ballistics is concerned with the flight path, or trajectory, of a projectile from the time it leaves the rifle or gun until landing. After a bullet has left the gun, it travels in an arc, falling downward because of gravity. The amount of air resistance to a projectile depends on the projectile's size, shape, speed, and on the density of air. Air resistance slows the projectile, reducing the range, or distance it travels. Winds and crosswinds can affect the range and direction of a projectile. If a projectile is fired from a moving weapon, or if the target is moving, the range can be affected. Electronic computers are used to measure the effects of all these factors.

Terminal ballistics is concerned with the effect of the projectile when it reaches its target. Bullets cause damage by penetration. Shell or bomb damage is caused by explosion. Nuclear missiles produce blast, heat, and radiation.

Forensic ballistics is a separate field that helps police to identify bullets. Every gun or rifle makes marks on the bullets it fires. No other gun or rifle can make the same marks on a bullet. Experts can find out whether or not a particular bullet was fired from a particular gun. Forensic ballistics has greatly aided police officers in identifying and arresting armed robbers and murderers.    J.J.A./J.T.

Any projectile, whether a shot from a gun, a missile, or a shot-put ball, as shown here, will travel farthest if the angle of push is 45°. At smaller or greater angles, the projectile will fall short for the same thrust.

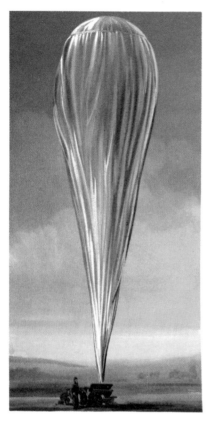

A scientific weather balloon is about to take off with special instruments that will be used to study conditions in the upper atmosphere.

Amateur ballooning is a popular pastime in many countries. Two hot-air balloons are shown above.

**BALLOON** (bə lün′) A balloon is a bag filled with hot air or a gas. A balloon rises and floats because the hot air or gas in the balloon is lighter than the air outside. Light materials, such as silk or plastic, are used in making balloons. Balloons may be either captive or free floating. A captive balloon is anchored to the ground by a line called a tether. A free-floating balloon travels in whatever direction the wind blows it. Many balloons have a basket, or gondola, attached below to carry passengers and equipment.

The first practical hot-air balloon was developed in France by two brothers, Joseph and Etienne Montgolfier. Their balloon was made of cloth and paper and had a diameter of about 11 m [35 ft]. They flew the balloon on

Left, a Thunderbird guided missile is checked out prior to testing. Inset photo, rear view showing aerodynamic stabilizers.

June 5, 1783. The first people to fly in a free-floating balloon were Jean-François Pilâtre de Rozier and François Laurent. They made their flight outside Paris in November 1783. The following month J.A.C. Charles and Nicolas Louis Robert made the world's first flight in a hydrogen-filled balloon. They rose to about 610 m [2,000 ft] and traveled about 40 km [25 mi].

There are two kinds of balloons—gas and hot-air. The main kinds of gas ballons are superpressure balloons, zero-pressure balloons, and expandable balloons. All three are used for scientific purposes.

In a superpressure balloon, the gas inside has a greater pressure than that of the air outside. When a superpressure balloon is launched, the bag is partly filled and then is sealed. The gas expands as the balloon rises. The bag of a superpressure balloon is not

Three American balloonists are shown aboard the *Double Eagle II* in flight and just after touch down near Paris, France. They completed the first successful transatlantic balloon crossing.

flexible, so once the bag is filled the balloon does not go any higher. The size of the bag determines how high the balloon will rise. Superpressure balloons can stay in the air for many months.

The gas inside a zero-pressure balloon is at the same pressure as that of the air on the outside. Once the balloon is aloft, the gas expands. If the gas expands too much, the excess gas escapes through a valve. In order to keep zero-pressure balloons in the air, ballast must be released from time to time. This is done by radio signals from the ground. Zero-pressure balloons usually fly for several days.

Expandable balloons are about 2m [6 ft] across when they lift off. As the balloon rises

and the gas expands, the bag may expand to about 6 m [20 ft]. When the balloon reaches the proper height, the bag bursts, and its instruments are returned to earth by parachute.

Gas balloons may be filled with hydrogen, helium, or natural gas. Natural gas is by far the cheapest, but it has the least lifting ability. Helium costs more than natural gas, but it is nonflammable and therefore very safe. Hydrogen has the greatest lifting ability, because it is the lightest gas. However, hydrogen can be dangerous because it is highly combustible.

Hot-air balloons work much the same way gas balloons do. The air in the bag is heated, making it lighter than the air outside. The air is heated by a propane-gas burner mounted below the bag. To make the balloon go up, more propane is burned. To lose altitude, less gas is burned.

Most balloons today are used to study weather and the atmosphere. However, sport ballooning is popular.

Balloons have been used in wars. Balloons were used by France in a war in 1870. They were also used in the American Civil War, World War I, and World War II. For the most part, captive balloons were used to observe the other side.

Much of the information we get about the weather is obtained from instruments carried by balloons. Weather researchers, or meteorologists, release balloons into the atmosphere to study the temperature, humidity, and pressure of the air at various altitudes. They use this information to forecast the weather. Balloons are also sent high into the stratosphere carrying instruments to record conditions such as cosmic radiation. These balloons may also carry telescopes and cameras. They have gone up as high as 43.5 km [27 mi].

Sport balloonists use both gas and hot-air balloons. Balloon races and rallies are held in many parts of the country. To get a ballooning license from the Federal Aviation Administration (FAA), a person must be at least sixteen years old, pass a written examination, and have ten hours of flying time with an instructor.

The record for the highest balloon flight was set in 1961 by two U.S. Navy officers—Commander Malcolm Ross and Lieutenant Commander Victor A. Prather, Jr. In the balloon *Lee Lewis Memorial*, they rose 34,668 m [113,739.9 ft].

The first people to cross the Atlantic Ocean in a balloon were Maxie Anderson, Ben Abruzzo, and Larry Newman. In August 1978 in the *Double Eagle II*, they lifted off from Presque Isle, Maine. They landed in Misery, France, slightly over 137 hours later. They had traveled 5,000 km [3,107 mi]. *See also* AVIATION, HISTORY OF.          J.J.A./J.VP.

**BALSAM** (bȯl′ səm) Balsam is an aromatic resin that comes from some trees and herbs. It is used mainly in the making of medicine, paints, perfume, and incense. Some balsams flow from herbs and trees. Other balsams must be gotten by cutting or breaking open herbs and trees. The balsam of Peru and balsam of Colombia are obtained from trees in South America. Both are commonly used in the making of perfumes. The Colombian balsam is also used in the making of throat syrup and lozenges. In North America, Canada balsam is taken from fir trees.   G.M.B./M.H.S.

**BAMBOO** (bam bü′) Bamboo is a member of the grass family Gramineae, which has 600 to 1,000 species. Bamboos are native to tropical climates. Growing from an underground root system called a rhizome, they grow very quickly. One bamboo reportedly grew 90 cm [3 ft] in 24 hours. Most bamboos are very tall—some as high as 37 m [120 ft]—and as thick as 30 cm [1 ft]. Bamboos have hollow wood stems. The leaves fall off as the plant grows. Some bamboos blossom only once in 30 years. Others may take 100 years to blossom. A bamboo plant dies after it blooms. The seeds from these blossoms grow into new plants.

Bamboo has been used to make many products. Some fishing poles are made from the stems of the plant. Bamboo stems have also been used to make rafts, furniture, and fences. In some countries, the young stems and rhizomes are pickled and eaten. The United States Department of Agriculture has a bamboo garden near Savannah, Georgia.   S.A.E./M.H.S.

**BANANA** (bə nan′ ə) Bananas are plants that grow in tropical regions. They grow 1.3–9 m [4–30 ft] in height. The banana looks like a palm tree. But it is not a tree. It does not have a woody stem or trunk. Instead, its leaves grow from a tough rootstock by which the plant spreads.

One large flower grows from the central stalk of the plant. This flower develops into the fruit. Each plant has one bunch of bananas, which can weigh as much as 45 kg [100 lb]. Cultivation of the banana has resulted in a fruit that has no seeds. New plants are started from cuttings from the old plant.

Bananas are cut while they are green. They are then loaded on trains to be transported to ships that carry them to many parts of the world. During shipment, they begin to mature and turn yellow. Brazil is the leading banana-growing country, producing as much as 5 million metric tons [5.5 million tons] a year. The United States imports more bananas than any other country.

Bananas are a nutritious food. They have great value in the treatment of certain diseases. They contain vitamins A and C and are rich in carbohydrates. Manila hemp is made from the fibers of some banana plants. It is used to make rope and certain fabrics.
P.G.C./F.W.S.

Bananas grow in bunches on trees in hot, damp regions such as South and Central America.

**BANDICOOT** (ban' di küt') Bandicoots make up a family of marsupials found in Australia and New Guinea. There are nineteen species. These ratlike mammals rarely grow to be larger than 0.6 m [2 ft]. The second and third toes are grown together. Like all marsupials, the bandicoot carries and nurses its young in a pouch. Only the bandicoot, however, has a pouch which opens at the bottom instead of at the top. The bandicoot is nocturnal. It sleeps in a burrow during the day and comes out to eat plants and insects at night.
A.J.C./R.J.B.

Bandicoots belong to a family of marsupials. They live in Australia and southeast Asia.

**BANTING, SIR FREDERICK GRANT** (1891–1941) Sir Frederick Banting (ban' ting) was a Canadian physician who discovered insulin, a hormone controlling the body's use of sugar. Working with Charles Best and others, Banting discovered this hormone by taking it out of the pancreas.

Banting's discovery led to a complete change in the treatment of diabetes. Diabetes is a disease that destroys or affects the ability of the body to use sugar. It causes large amounts of sugar to appear in the urine. Banting and a partner, J. J. Macleod, won the 1923 Nobel Prize for medicine for the discovery of insulin. Banting shared his prize with Charles Best, a fellow researcher, a striking example of scientific brotherhood.
J.J.A./D.G.F.

**BANYAN** (ban' yən) The banyan is a member of the mulberry family which produces figlike fruits. Its scientific name is *Ficus benghalensis*. It is found in tropical Asia and Africa. The banyan may grow as tall as 35 m [115.5 ft]. It has roots growing down from its branches into the ground. Because of this unique root system, some banyans may cover an acre or more, even though the original roots may have died. Some varieties of banyans are epiphytes and grow onto other trees in order to support their roots.

A.J.C./M.H.S.

**BARBERRY FAMILY** (bär′ ber′ ē) The barberry family is a group of about 500 species of spiny shrubs that are dicotyledons. They grow from 1 to 3.7 m [3 to 12 ft] high. Barberry shrubs are native to the temperate zones of the northern hemisphere. They are most frequently planted by landscapers for hedges and other landscape features. They have yellow wood and yellow flowers. The berries are red, yellow, blue, purple, or black. The berries of most species can be made into jellies. A yellow dye is found in some of the barberry plants of Asia and South America.

In the United States, the best known kinds of barberries are the common barberry, the Japanese barberry, and the wintergreen barberry. The common barberry is attacked by spring stem rust, which is very harmful to wheat. For this reason, there are laws in the wheat-growing areas of the United States that prohibit the growing of barberry.

G.M.B./M.H.S.

**BARBITURATE** (bär bich′ ə rət) A barbiturate is a drug used to calm people or to help them sleep. Barbiturates slow down brain activity and the rest of the nervous system. In the United States, barbiturates can be obtained legally only with a doctor's prescription.

Barbiturates are made from barbituric acid. They may come in a tablet or capsule form and sometimes as a powder or liquid. Barbiturates are different in strength and in the length of time they affect people. Different people may have different reactions to taking the same amount of the same barbiturate.

Regular use of barbiturates causes addiction. Some people take large amounts of barbiturates to escape tension. Large doses make the user's speech become slurred, and coordination and judgment become poor. A person can die from an overdose of barbiturates. When an addicted person tries to stop taking barbiturates, he becomes extremely nervous. His body may shake and twitch violently. An immediate stopping of the use of barbiturates can cause death. An addict can end his dependence of the drugs usually by gradually reducing the amount he has been taking.

The first barbiturate used in medicine was barbital. It appeared in 1903 under the name Veronal. Next came phenobarbital in 1912, under the name Luminal. There are more than 25 kinds of barbiturates being used today. The barbiturates that are used to calm people and to help bring sleep include amobarbital (Amytal) and pentobarbital (Nembutal). Surgeons use some types of barbiturates as anesthetics when performing operations. Phenobarbital and other barbiturates help prevent seizures of epilepsy. Barbiturates are also used to relax mentally ill patients, calming them so they can talk over their problems with their doctors.

J.J.A./J.J.F.

**BARIUM** (bar′ ē əm) Barium is a soft, silvery metallic element. Barium's symbol is Ba. Its atomic number is 56. Its atomic weight is 137.3. Barium melts at 725°C [1,337°F] and boils at 1,640°C [2,984°F]. Its relative density is 3.5. Barium is one of the alkaline earth metals. It was discovered in 1808 by Sir Humphrey Davy, an English scientist. It is found most often in a mineral called barite. It is extracted from barite by electrolysis.

Barium is a very reactive metal and is almost never found in a pure state. This is because it reacts with the oxygen in the air. Pure barium has very few uses, but its compounds are widely used. Doctors use barium sulfate in x-ray examinations. They feed it to you when they want to x-ray your intestines. This is called a barium meal. The barium sulfate absorbs x-rays and the intestines show up white on the photograph. Barium nitrate is used in fireworks to give a green flame. Barium carbonate is used in ceramics and glass. M.E./J.R.W.

**BARK** (bärk) Bark is the protective outer covering of tree branches, trunks, and roots. Bark has three layers. The outer periderm is made of dead cells such as cork. Periderm is usually thick. It protects the tree against weather, insects, and disease. The middle cortex layer is made of living, non-growing cells. The innermost phloem brings food made in the leaves down to the roots. The periderm of some trees has small openings called lenticels. Lenticels allow gases such as oxygen and carbon dioxide to enter and leave the plant.

Bark is used mainly for its cork. Quinine, cough medicine, cinnamon, and other useful substances are also obtained from bark. *See also* CORTEX; PHLOEM. A.J.C./M.H.S.

Barley is an important cereal. Some is used for making beer, but most barley is fed to animals.

**BARLEY** (bär′ lē) Barley is a widely used cereal plant of the genus *Hordeum*. This genus, having 16 species, is a member of the grass family. Barleys are found in Europe, Asia, North Africa, and North America. Barley heads usually have long, bristly flowers which grow in tightly bunched spikes, with three additional spikes at each node. Most barleys are weeds. One species, called squirrel tail grass, is grown for use as an ornament.

Barley grown as a crop comes from three species, with two, four, or six rows of grain on the spike. In the most common type, the single grains grow in three rows on each side of the spike. These are called six-rowed barleys. Two-rowed barleys are less common. The four and six-rowed barleys are the older kinds, grown since people started farming for food and making beer.

Barley thrives in cool climates. In warmer climates, barley is planted as a winter crop. Spring barley is planted in spring and matures by summer. Winter barley is planted in fall and harvested the next summer. The grain should be harvested when it is dry enough so that a kernel snaps when bitten. Barley can be grown in the same place for many years if the soil is properly fed, and if the barley does not succumb to diseases or soil erosion. The world produces about 7,120,000,000 bushels of barley a year. Russia is the largest producer.

In the United States, about 65% of the barley grown is used for animal feed. High-quality barley may be made into malt. Malt is used in beer, liquor, malted milk, and flavorings. Pearled barley is made by removing the husk and polishing the grain. Pearled barley is used to thicken soups. By-products of pearling include barley flour and animal feed. Barley flour may be used in baby cereal and in bread. J.J.A./F.W.S.

**BARNACLE** (bär′ ni kəl) Barnacles are saltwater crustaceans that spend their entire adult lives attached to underwater objects. Barnacles have been found on rocks, turtles, whales, buoys, and ship bottoms. There are about 800 species of this crustacean. Most grow a hard, stony covering around themselves for protection. This covering has an opening for the barnacle's legs. Barnacles capture microscopic plants and animals by waving their legs out this opening. The motion of their legs also brings dissolved oxygen into the shell. When in danger, the barnacle pulls in its legs and hides in the shell.

Barnacles have three life stages. In the first, they are small, free-swimming creatures with one eye. In the second stage, they have 6 pairs of legs, paired eyes, and 2 feelers. In the third stage, they still have 12 legs, but they lose their eyes. They attach themselves to underwater objects during this stage.

Barnacles that attach themselves to the bottoms of ships cause serious problems. They slow the ship by increasing the ship's resistance to the water. They also add weight. Barnacles may increase the weight of an ocean liner by several tons. This is known as the fouling problem. *See also* PLANKTON.

A.J.C./C.S.H.

Barnacles are crustaceans with an unusual life history. Their larvae and early stages are free-swimming. But the adult lives attached to a rock, feeding through its legs. It is described as standing on its head while kicking food into its mouth.

**BARNARD, CHRISTIAAN NEETHLING** (1922-      ) Dr. Christiaan Barnard (bär′-nərd) is a South African surgeon who performed the first human heart transplant operation. On December 3, 1967, he transplanted a heart into 55-year-old Louis Washkansky. The heart had belonged to a 25-year-old woman who had died in an automobile accident. Washkansky lived for 18 days but finally died of a lung infection. Barnard has since performed many such operations. In 1974, he transplanted a human heart into a patient without removing the patient's own heart. He joined the donor heart to the patient's heart, providing a ''double pump'' for the circulatory system. Barnard also experimented with transplanting animal hearts into human beings.

The techniques that Barnard developed have been greatly improved. By the mid-1970s, 50% of the patients operated on by a Stanford University medical team survived the first year. *See also* TRANSPLANTATION.

A.J.C./D.G.F.

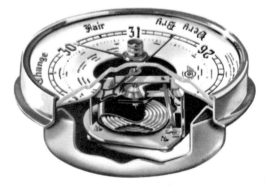

Cutaway drawing of an aneroid barometer. This instrument consists of a thin-walled metal box containing a partial vacuum. Changes in air pressure cause the internal parts of the box to expand or contract, moving the pointer.

**BAROMETER** (bə räm′ ət ər) A barometer is a device that measures air pressure. It is used to help forecast the weather and to measure the altitude, or height, of objects and locations above sea level.

In 1643, an Italian, Evangelista Torricelli, showed that the weight of air pressing down on mercury would push it to a certain height in a tube. He was able to show that air pressure at sea level is normally 76 cm [30 in], the height mercury rises in a tube that has a diameter of 1 cm [0.3937 in]. Other scientists then reasoned that altitude could be measured by observing changes in the height of the mercury at different locations. Since air is thinner at great heights, they believed its pressure would support less mercury as height increased. The higher above sea level, the lower the column of mercury would be. This was proven to be true. Today, barometers are used in airplanes to measure altitude. They are called altimeters.

In a mercury barometer, a printed scale beside the tube containing mercury gives the barometric reading, or measurement. It may be written in inches, centimeters, or both.

In 1939, the United States Weather Bureau adopted the bar as a unit of measurement. It gives a more exact pressure reading at sea level of 75.01 cm [29.53 in]. Scientists now measure air pressure in millibars. One millibar equals a column of mercury .08 cm [.03 in] high in a tube with a diameter of 1 cm [.39 in], or 1/1,000 of a bar.

A mercury barometer is used for weather forecasting. When the mercury drops rapidly, a storm is forecast. When the mercury rises steadily, good weather is forecast.

Aneroid barometers use no liquid. They show air pressure by recording its effect on an airtight box that has had some of its air taken out. The sides of the box move in and out according to the amount of air pressure on them. The movements of the sides are recorded by a pointer which moves across a scale. Aneroid barometers are smaller than mercury barometers and easier to carry.

The barograph is an aneroid barometer that scientists use to keep records of changes in air pressure. The barograph records air pressure on paper that is attached to a revolving drum. *See also* ATMOSPHERE; WEATHER.

H.G./C.R.

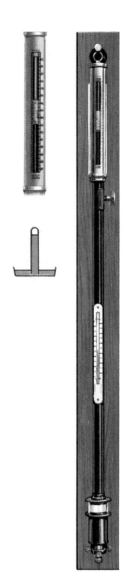

The Fortin mercury barometer. This instrument consists of a glass tube, open at one end, that is filled with mercury. When turned upside down and immersed in a container of mercury (see small diagram), the mercury in the tube falls only a little bit because the air pressure on the surface of the mercury in the container holds up the mercury column. The top part of the tube has very little air—it is a partial vacuum. Changes in air pressure, or in the weather, cause the height of the mercury column to rise or fall. The height is measured in inches or in millimeters, using the brass vernier (shown at the right) on the barometer.

**BARRACUDA** (bar′ ə küd′ ə) The barracuda is a saltwater fish belonging to the family Sphyraenidae. It is a long, slender fish with many large, sharp teeth. Barracuda are found in coastal waters of warm seas throughout the world. There are five species of barracuda in North American waters. The great barracuda, which lives off the coast of Florida, may reach lengths of 2.5 m [8 ft]. Although it is considered dangerous by many skin divers, very few instances have been recorded of the barracuda attacking swimmers. S.R.G./E.C.M.

**BASALT** (bə sölt′) Basalt is a heavy, black or gray igneous rock made of tiny grains. The

Basalt is a familiar volcanic rock. It often forms columns, as in the Giant's Causeway, Ireland.

grains are crystals, usually made of the minerals plagioclase and pyroxene. Basalt is formed from lava, the red-hot liquid from volcanoes. Basalt is the most common volcanic rock. Hawaii, Samoa, and Tahiti are volcanic islands formed of basalt.

When lava cools and hardens to form basalt, the basalt can split in columns, resembling giant stepping stones on the surface. Cliffs having basalt columns are among famous tourist attractions. One is the Devil's Postpile in California; another, the Giant's Causeway in Northern Ireland. Some large basalt fields have been built up by lava flowing from narrow openings in the ground. On the Columbia Plateau, a basalt field in the state of Washington, the basalt is about 1,000 m [3,300 ft] or more in thickness.

Crushed basalt is used for roadmaking and as building stone. *See also* ROCK; VOLCANO.

J.J.A./R.H.

**BASE** (bās) In chemistry, a base is often described as a compound that can combine with an acid to form a salt. Acids produce hydrogen ions ($H^+$) when they are dissolved in water or other solvents. Bases produce basic ions that combine with hydride ions. The most common basic ion is the hydroxal ion (OH)–. Bases are called proton acceptors. Acids are called proton donors.

Most bases contain atoms of a metal and one or more hydroxyl (OH–) groups. These bases are formed when a metal oxide reacts with water. Bases in water solution taste bitter and feel slippery. They turn red litmus paper blue. Bases ionize, or break down, into positive and negative ions. A strong base, such as sodium hydroxide (NaOH), breaks down almost completely in solution. (*See* SOLUTION AND SOLUBILITY.) Such bases are called alkalis. A weak base, such as ammonium hydroxide ($NH_4OH$), ionizes (breaks down) only slightly in water. Bases have a pH from 7 to 14. The stronger the base, the higher the pH number.

The bases sodium hydroxide (caustic soda) and potassium hydroxide (caustic potash) are used in making soap, paper, bleach, and many kinds of chemicals. Along with ammonium hydroxide or ammonia solution, they are useful cleaning agents because they cause reactions that remove grease. Calcium oxide (quicklime) is used to make glass, and calcium hydroxide (slaked lime) to make mortar. *See also* ACID.          J.J.A./A.D.

**BASIDIUM** (bə sid′ ē əm) The basidium is the sexual reproductive structure in Basidiomycetes, an advanced class of fungi. Common varieties of these fungi are mushrooms and puffballs. Each fungus contains hundreds of the teardrop-shaped basidia. Each basidium contains four spores. Once the spores are released, the fungus dies. Each of these spores may produce a new fungus. *See also* FUNGUS; MUSHROOM.          A.J.C./M.H.S.

Plantlike in appearance, basket stars are actually marine animals. They are related to the starfish.

**BASKET STAR** (bas′ kət stär′) The basket star is a marine echinoderm. It is a member of the class Ophiuroidea. (*See* ECHINODERMATA.) The basket star gets its name from its star-shaped body and its five long arms. Each of these arms branches off into other arms, making this organism look like a basket. These arms are used to gather detritus for food. The basket star lives on the ocean floor. *See also* BRITTLE STAR.          A.J.C./C.S.H.

**BASS** (bas) Bass is the name given to several kinds of fish. True basses are saltwater fishes belonging to the Percichythyidae and Serranidae families. Well-known examples are the striped bass, channel bass, and grouper.

Better known, however, are the freshwater basses. They belong to the sunfish family,

Centrarchidae. The largemouth bass and smallmouth bass are especially popular game fishes sought by fisherman. They were originally found only in the southern and central United States. They have since been taken to waters in every state and to many countries around the world. The world's record largemouth bass weighed 10.9 kg [24 lb, 4 oz]. It was caught in Georgia S.R.G./E.C.M.

**BAT** (bat) Bats are the only mammals that can fly. Their wings are actually long arms and fingers covered with a thin skin that connects down the body to the lower leg. Like other mammals, they have legs, but they do not walk on them. They depend almost entirely on flying, using their legs and feet when they hang upside down in a roosting position.

Bats are furry animals that usually look like mice. They vary in size. The smallest have bodies 3.8 cm [1.5 in] long with a wingspread of about 15 cm [6 in]. The largest may be 30 cm [12 in] long and have a wingspread of 1.8 m [6 ft]. Some bats, depending on the shape and length of their wings, can fly as fast as 24 kph [15 mph]. The smaller ones fly around 8 to 13 kph [5 to 8 mph].

Much is known about bat behavior. They have nocturnal habits, sleeping during the day and flying at night in search of food. They live together in colonies and roost in trees and caves. Their food consists of insects and fruits. Because most species eat insects, bats are generally considered beneficial to humankind.

A very interesting part of bat behavior is how they navigate at night in search of food. They have very poor vision and cannot see well in the dark. They fly and locate food using a system called echolocation. They send out very high sounds, in the form of short bursts. The sounds are too high-pitched for human beings to hear. The sounds bounce off objects and return as echoes, helping the animals to determine the direction and distance of anything in their paths. Bats can detect and catch insects in the air. Experiments in the laboratory show they are even able to locate and avoid hitting very fine wires strung in their way. This system of echolocation is similar to the sonar and radar systems developed by people for navigation under the sea and in the air.

Bats usually mate in the fall. The young are born in the springtime. The females may have from one to four babies a year, depending on the kind of bat. Because bats do not build nests, infant bats must cling to their mothers for several weeks. During this time, the young are given thorough training in flying and hunting.

There are many species of bats living all over the world. The most common kinds to be found in North America are the brown bats, the Mexican free-tailed bats, the hoary bats, and the silver-haired bats.

A common kind found in Central and South America is the vampire bat. It is known especially for its unique habit of feeding on the blood of other animals, mainly cattle. The vampire bat digs into the skin of its prey with sharp bites, then licks the blood from the wound. The vampire bat drinks about 15 ml [42 oz] of blood each day. They are dangerous to people and animals only if they carry the disease rabies.                    P.G.C./J.J.M.

Bats are flying mammals that navigate by sound waves. They pick up echoes of their squeaks.

**BATHOLITH** (bath′ ə lith′) A batholith is a huge body of rock formed by the forcing and hardening of material moving upward from the earth's interior into the crust. The surface of a batholith is usually more than 100 sq km [40 sq mi]. It may be much larger. Masses covering less than 100 sq km are called stocks.

Forced up from the earth's interior, batholiths are dome-shaped structures. They were once thought to have unknown depth. Recent studies show that many of them have floors, with a thickness of at least 1,000 m [3,300 ft]. Rocks lying on top of a batholith may be forced upward into an arch. Batholiths are seen only when the overlying rocks have been worn away. *See also* IGNEOUS ROCK.

J.J.A./W.R.S.

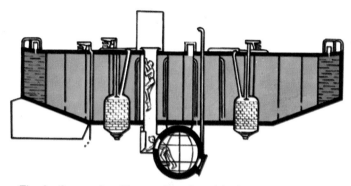

The bathyscaphe. The explorer's cabin is a heavy steel sphere. Two tanks (red) filled with air help float the craft. When these tanks are flooded, the weight of heavy iron shot in the hull causes the vessel to sink. Releasing the shot enables the bathyscaphe to return to the surface.

**BATHYSPHERE AND BATHYSCAPHE**
A bathysphere (bath′ i sfir′) is a hollow steel ball with portholes, once used for deep-sea exploring. It is large enough to hold one person inside. The bathysphere was designed by Otis Barton, an American. It was used in the 1930s and 1940s to go down as far as 1,000 m [3,300 ft] under the sea. The bathysphere, attached to a ship by a cable, was always being knocked around as the ship was tossed about on the waves.

The bathyscaphe (bath′ i skaf′) was designed to overcome this problem. It was invented by August Piccard, a Swiss scientist, who was famous for his balloon flights into the stratosphere. The bathyscaphe is free-floating. It is supported by a large float tank filled with gasoline. Piccard started work in 1939. In 1948, he dived in his bathyscaphe *FNRS* to a depth of more than 1,524 m [5,000 ft]. His later, improved bathyscaphe, *Trieste*, was bought by the United States Navy. The *Trieste* went down 10,912 m [35,800 ft] into the Marianas Trench in the Pacific in 1960.

Research and development programs for deep-diving vehicles have continued. Their goals are related to national defense, the need for services like search and rescue, salvage operations, and the promise of new resources from the ocean. J.J.A./R.W.L.

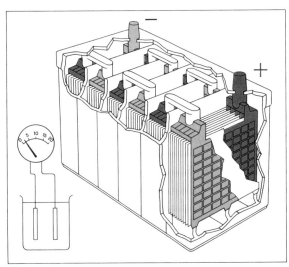

A lead-acid battery, the kind used in automobiles. This battery has six cells, each of which has a positive electrode (red) and a negative electrode (blue). Each cell provides about two volts, as shown in the smaller diagram. The lead electrodes are immersed in sulfuric acid diluted with water. The battery is charged by passing electricity through it. When in operation, electrons flow from the negative pole to the positive pole.

# BATTERY

A battery (bat′ ə rē) is a device that produces electricity by chemical action. A battery contains one or more units called cells. Each cell can produce electric current. Single cell batteries are used to power flashlights and toys.

Batteries with several cells provide electricity for automobiles, heavy equipment, spacecraft, submarines, and emergency electric lights.

The first battery was developed in the late 1790s by Count Alessandro Volta, an Italian scientist. In 1859, a French physicist, Gaston Plante, invented the first lead-acid storage battery. Another French scientist, George Leclanche, introduced the first dry cell battery a few years later.

Primary or dry cell batteries do not have long lives. They stop giving off electricity when their chemicals lose their power. These batteries usually consist of one cell. Secondary or wet cell batteries can be used for years. They can be recharged many times after they are first discharged. They usually consist of several cells.

Batteries come in many sizes. Tiny ones used to power electric watches and hearing aids weigh as little 1.4 g [0.05 oz]. Huge batteries used in submarines weigh up to 0.91 metric tons [1 short ton]. The average automobile storage battery weighs about 16 to 18 kg [35 to 40 lbs].

Batteries differ in voltages, or power. A typical flashlight battery produces 1½ volts.

**Dry cell batteries**   Millions of dry cell batteries are manufactured each year. They contain rodlike structures called electrodes. A thick, pastelike chemical substance, or electrolyte, surrounds the electrodes. (*See* ELECTROLYSIS.) The zinc casings of dry cells also act as electrodes. Chemical reaction between the electrolyte and the electrodes creates an electric charge, or voltage difference, between the electrodes. When a device is attached to the electrodes, the current flows from one electrode to the other, making the device work.

There are three main types of dry cell batteries: carbon-zinc, alkaline, and mercury. The carbon-zinc battery was developed first. Most flashlight batteries are of the carbon-zinc type. The rodlike electrode is made of carbon. The other electrode is the zinc casing. The electrolyte is composed of ammonium chloride, zinc chloride, and water. Carbon-zinc batteries can be recharged. However, the charge only lasts a short time.

An alkaline dry cell battery is more powerful. It lasts five to eight times longer than a carbon-zinc battery. It has a carbon electrode and a zinc casing electrode. The electrolyte is a strong alkali solution, potassium hydroxide. Alkaline dry cells are used mainly for portable radios.

In a mercury dry cell, the voltage remains constant to the end of the battery's life. A mercuric oxide electrode is used. The other electrode is the zinc casing. The electrolyte is potassium hydroxide.

**Wet cell batteries** Wet cell or storage batteries produce much more electricity than dry cell batteries. They are large in size and can be recharged many times. There are two main types of storage batteries: lead-acid and nickel-cadmium.

Lead-acid batteries consist of plastic or hard rubber containers with three or six cells. Each cell contains two sets of electrodes. One set is positive. The other set is negative. The electrolyte is a mixture of sulfuric acid and water. Chemical reaction causes an electric charge to build up at the electrodes. Each cell generates two volts of electricity. Most automobile storage batteries contain six cells that generate a total of 12 volts. A recent development in lead-acid batteries is the maintenance-free battery. It does not require the periodic addition of water. It lasts longer because its electrodes are made of alloys containing lead, calcium, and tin. Unlike the electrodes in regular lead-acid batteries, these electrodes do not cause the battery to discharge, or lose its power, when it is not in use.

Nickel cadmium storage batteries operate on the same general principles as lead-acid batteries but contain a different electrolyte and different electrodes. The electrolyte is a solution of potassium hydroxide. The positive electrodes are made of nickel oxide and the negative electrodes are made of cadmium. Nickel cadmium batteries can be sealed airtight. They do not require periodic additions of water. This makes them ideal for use in portable tools and equipment and in space satellites. *See also* ELECTRICITY; FUEL CELL.

W.R.P./L.L.R.

**BAYBERRY** (bā′ ber′ ē) The bayberry is a West Indian tree. Its leaves produce bay oil. Bay oil is used in making perfumes and bay rum. This tree is also called the wild cinnamon tree.

The name bayberry is also given to a shrub found along the North American seacoasts. Its bark can be used to make a liquid which is used in medicine.     A.J.C./M.H.S.

**BEADLE, GEORGE WELLS** (1903–    ) George Wells Beadle (bē′ dəl) is an American scientist who works in the field of genetics. In 1958, he and his co-worker, Edward L. Tatum, won the Nobel Prize for Medicine for discoveries that helped explain how genes work. Beadle used a form of bread mold. By using x-rays on the mold, he was able to show that irradiated genes have different chemical changes in their enzymes from genes that have not been irradiated. His experiments proved that genes control the making of enzymes. *See also* IRRADIATION.

P.G.C./D.G.F.

**BEAN** (bēn) The bean plant is a member of the pea family. Beans are an important source of nitrogen in the diet. Several different types of beans are grown widely for human use or animal feed. Beans vary in size, color, and tenderness.

The most important type of bean grown in the United States is the soybean. Other types include the scarlet runner bean and the kidney bean. The lima bean is grown mainly in Central America and the midwestern United States.

The bean plant grows as a shrub or as a tall climbing vine. Before the beans are ready to be picked, the plant usually has brightly colored flowers. The bean plant grows best in warm, moist climates.     A.J.C./J.R.

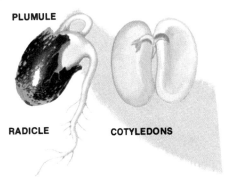

PLUMULE

RADICLE     COTYLEDONS

The runner bean seed is shown germinating on the left and split open at the right. It has large, fleshy cotyledons, or seed leaves; a small radicle, or young root, and a plumule, or young shoot.

**BEAR** (ber) Bears belong to the family Ursidae. They are the largest carnivores living on land. Most bears live north of the equator. No wild bears live in Antarctica, Africa, or Australia. Although they are adapted for eating meat, most bears also eat plants. Bears have large, heavy, fur-covered bodies and short, strong legs. Each paw has five toes. Each of these toes ends in a long, heavy claw. These claws are always exposed and are used for feeding, digging, and fighting. The bottoms of the paws are hairless. Bears range in size from the sun bear at 30 kg [66 lb] to the Alaskan brown bear at 780 kg [1,700 lb]. Although bears appear to be large and clumsy, they are able to run and swim quickly.

Bears have small, weak eyes. Although their hearing is good, they rely almost entirely on their sense of smell. Bears have 42 teeth. Some are for tearing meat, others are for chewing it. Bears are fairly intelligent and can be trained to perform simple tricks. All bears, even tame ones, are very protective. They will attack any person or animal that threatens them, their food, their homes, or their cubs.

Bears do not hibernate. Before the winter, they gain weight and find a cave or other suitable shelter. They sleep fitfully during the winter months. They may even wake up and wander around on warm days. Bears usually live alone. They never travel in groups. A male bear will stay with a female for about a month. Shortly after mating, the male leaves. The female is then left alone to find shelter for herself and her unborn cubs. Two cubs are usually born during the winter. Some females may give birth to as many as four cubs. The cubs are born hairless and weigh less than 0.5 kg [1 lb]. They stay with the mother for two years. During this time, the mother teaches them to hunt and to care for themselves. *See also* BLACK BEAR; BROWN BEAR; GRIZZLY BEAR; KODIAK BEAR; POLAR BEAR.

A.J.C./J.J.M.

**BEARING** (ber′ ing) A bearing is the part of a machine that supports a moving part, reducing the friction, or rubbing, as much as possible. Bearings are made from a metal that is softer than the moving part. Bearings wear out faster than the moving parts, and are easier to replace. Many bearings are lined with a soft metal called Babbitt metal.

The most common types of bearings are the ball and roller bearings. These bearings depend on the principle that rolling produces a lot less friction than sliding. The revolving pivot, or journal, inside a ball bearing works upon a number of smaller steel balls. The balls roll easily in a track called the race. These balls are in a frame that keeps them apart from each other but allows contact with the moving parts of the machine. Roller bearings are similar but have rollers shaped like cylinders or tapered cones instead of balls. The rollers usually lie side by side around the shaft.

The plain, or oil-film, bearing consists of a shaft inside a shell of softer metal. The plain bearing is often called the sleeve bearing, as it fits around the shaft like a coat sleeve. A film of oil covers both the bearing and the shaft to help reduce friction. The softer lining is usually made of Babbitt metal, but copper and lead alloys are also widely used. Nylon bearings are used for much lighter load work. Friction between plastics and metal is quite low, and water can be used as a lubricant.

Some machines, like a refrigerator motor, use self-lubricating bearings because the machine cannot be lubricated after assembly. The jewel bearing, used in watches and airplane instruments, has a pivot often made of crystal or a gemstone, such as ruby.

Wheels turn in bearings as they turn on their axles. The piston driving the wheels of a steam locomotive slides back and forth in a bearing. Almost all of the machinery used in modern civilization moves on bearings.

J.J.A./R.W.L.

Examples of two kinds of bearings. Top, ball bearings; bottom, roller bearings.

**BEATS** (bēts) Beats are regular variations in the loudness of a sound. They occur when two sound waves of almost the same pitch overlap. The pitch of a sound is controlled by its frequency. Suppose that two sounds have frequencies of 440 hertz (cycles per second) and 442 hertz. If the waves overlap they combine to form a sound whose frequency is midway between the two. Its frequency is 441 hertz. The loudness of this sound increases and decreases. The number of beats you hear is equal to the difference in the frequencies of the two sounds. In this case, there are two beats per second.

Beats are caused by interference between the two sound waves. When the two waves reinforce each other, they make a loud sound. When they cancel each other out, the sound is soft. The same thing sometimes happens between two light waves. They can interfere to produce patterns of light and dark. This is also a form of beats. *See also* HERTZ. M.E./J.T.

**BEAUFORT SCALE** (bō′ fərt skāl′) The Beaufort scale is a system of describing the velocity of winds. Rear Admiral Sir Francis Beaufort of the British navy created the scale in 1805. It was originally used at sea but has been changed so that it may now be used on land as well. A person may learn the approximate speed of the wind from the chart by noticing the wind's effects. For example, a wind that begins to break twigs off of trees is a fresh gale with the Beaufort number 8. A more exact measure of the speed of the wind is now found by using instruments. (*See* ANEMOMETER.) S.R.G./C.R.

**BEAVER** (bē′ vər) The beaver is a rodent with a large, thickset body and short strong legs. The hind feet are webbed for swimming. The forefeet do not have webs. The beaver uses its forefeet almost like hands. Its tail is broad and flat like a paddle and is of great use in swimming. The beaver's body can reach a

| THE BEAUFORT SCALE FOR WIND CLASSIFICATION | | | | |
|---|---|---|---|---|
| Beaufort Number | Speed mph | Speed kph | Description | Effects |
| 0 | 0-1 | 0-1 | Calm | Smoke rises vertically |
| 1 | 1-3 | 1-5 | Light air | Wind direction shown by drift of smoke |
| 2 | 4-7 | 6-11 | Slight breeze | Wind felt on face; leaves rustle; wind vanes moved |
| 3 | 8-12 | 12-19 | Gentle breeze | Leaves and twigs in constant motion; light flags extended |
| 4 | 13-18 | 20-28 | Moderate breeze | Dust and small branches move; flags flap |
| 5 | 19-24 | 29-38 | Fresh breeze | Small trees sway; small waves on lakes and streams |
| 6 | 25-31 | 39-49 | Strong breeze | Large branches move; hard to use umbrellas |
| 7 | 32-38 | 50-61 | Moderate gale | Large trees sway |
| 8 | 39-46 | 62-74 | Fresh gale | Twigs break off trees; walking becomes difficult |
| 9 | 47-54 | 75-88 | Strong gale | Slight damage to houses (slates removed) |
| 10 | 55-63 | 89-102 | Whole gale | Trees uprooted; much damage to houses |
| 11 | 64-75 | 103-117 | Storm | Widespread damage |
| 12 | over 75 | over 117 | Hurricane | Violent conditions; sometimes loss of life |

The Beaufort number used to describe a particular wind condition tells more than the approximate speed of the air mass. Number 10 of the Beaufort Scale indicates "whole gale," damage to houses and trees by wind that is blowing in the range of 55 to 63 miles per hour. The top of the scale is 12, indicating hurricane conditions.

length of 90 cm [3 ft] and can weigh as much as 27 kg [60 lb].

Beavers are aquatic animals. They live in and around lakes and streams and are common in the northern United States and in Canada. Observers of the behavior of the beaver are impressed with the animal's ability to build dams, lodges, and canals. Beavers have been called the engineers of the animal kingdom.

Beavers build dams across streams to form artificial lakes. They build their homes, called lodges, in these lakes. If the stream is quiet, they build the dam straight across it. If the stream has a strong current, they bow the dam in an inward curve so it can stand the pressure of the water.

Dams are built out of parts of trees cut down by the beavers with their sharp teeth. They float logs, limbs, and twigs of the trees into place where the dam is to be built. They interweave the limbs and twigs together and cover the structure with a mortar of clay and dead leaves. Beavers start their dams during the summer months when the level of the water is lowest. They continue construction until the first cold weather. They constantly repair the dams.

The lodges are built on the banks of the lake, in shallow areas in ponds, or on a small island. They look like large mud heaps but are constructed just like the dams. The beavers enter the inside of the lodge through a tunnel that comes up from below the level of the water. They use a second tunnel to bring in food for the winter.

In a Canadian national park, during a period of fifteen months, two beavers cut down 226 trees; built three dams of 15 m [50 ft] wide across a river; constructed a lodge of 28 cu m [1,000 cu ft]; and stored up bark, roots, and twigs for winter food in a pile of 20 cu m [720 cu ft].

Beavers live together in families. The females have litters of two to four kits that stay with the families until they are two years old. They then go out to mate and start families of their own.

At one time, millions of beavers lived in North America. They were hunted for their valuable fur until laws were passed to protect

The beaver is the second largest rodent, exceeded in size only by the capybara.

them. Now, because they are protected, the number of beavers has greatly increased in some parts of the United States.

P.G.C./J.J.M.

**BECQUEREL, ANTOINE HENRI (1852–1908)** Henri Becquerel (bek rel′) was a French physicist who discovered radioactivity. Becquerel's father and grandfather were also physicists. His grandfather made several important discoveries in electrochemistry. His father worked with fluorescence and phosphorescence. Becquerel also worked with fluorescent substances, trying to find out if they gave off X rays. At one time, he accidentally placed in a drawer some crystals of pitchblende next to some photographic film. Later on he noticed that rays affecting the film were coming from an element in the pitchblende. This radioactive element was uranium. Becquerel showed his discovery to Madame Curie, who called the occurrence ''radio activity.'' This led Curie to the discovery of radium, another radioactive element found in pitchblende. In 1903, Becquerel shared with Madame Curie and her husband Pierre the Nobel prize in physics.

J.J.A./D.G.F.

The bedbug is a parasite.

**BEDBUG** (bed′ bəg′) Bedbugs are small insects that feed on the blood of humans and other animals. They are usually found in the homes of people who are not careful to keep their houses clean. The bedbug pierces the skin of its victim with its sharp beak. Then it sucks up blood. Some humans suffer swelling and itching from the bites of bedbugs.

Bedbugs are about 6 mm [.25 in] long and reddish brown. They have wings that are too small for flying. They usually come out at night. During the day they hide in bedding, bed clothes, furniture, cracks in the wall, or under the floor. The adult bedbug lays between 100 and 250 eggs. The eggs hatch in about two weeks. Bedbugs live as long as a year.

Because of improved personal hygiene and better living conditions, bedbugs are now gradually disappearing. *See also* PARASITE.

G.M.B./J.R.

# BEE

Bees (bēz) are insects that belong to the order Hymenoptera. They are related to ants and wasps. There are many species of bees found all over the world. The body of a bee, which is seldom longer than 3.75 cm [1.5 in], has three parts: a head, a thorax, and an abdomen. Two pairs of wings are attached to the thorax. Female bees have an ovipositor at the end of their abdomen. They use the ovipositor to lay eggs and to sting enemies. Bees are probably best known for their stings and for their honey.

Bees collect a sugary solution called nectar from flowers. They produce honey from the nectar. Honey is their major source of food. While the bee is collecting the nectar, it carries pollen from one flower to another. This results in pollination of the flower. Pollination is necessary to most plants, so bees are important to flower and vegetable gardens. (*See* POLLINATION.)

Hatching bees undergo a metamorphosis. A larva hatches and turns into a pupa, which changes into an adult bee. The larva, pupa, and adult all look different. (*See* INSECT.)

There are solitary bees and social bees. There are many more kinds of solitary bees than there are kinds of social bees. Most solitary

A honeybee collecting nectar and pollen. These materials are carried back to the hive in special organs. Bees are important agents for fertilizing plants.

bees live alone. When they do live together, they do not divide up the work in the hive as social bees do. Some solitary bees, like the carpenter bee, make their nests in wood. Most build their nests underground. Each female solitary bee builds her own nest. It has many cells, or holes, in it. The bee puts honey and nectar in the cells and then lays an egg in each one. After covering the cells, she leaves to build other nests. The honey in the cells provides food for the young bees which hatch from the eggs.

Social bees live together in large numbers. Their nests are called hives. Some social bees, like the honeybee, build their hives in dead trees. Social bees divide their work into many different jobs. Different types of bees do different types of jobs.

**Bumblebees** One of the better-known social bees is the bumblebee. It belongs to the family Apidae. It has a thick, hairy body sometimes reaching 3.75 cm [1.5 in] in length. It is colored with yellow and black stripes. A queen bumblebee moves in to holes or abandoned animal nests in the spring and prepares a cell from the wax within her body. She then collects some pollen, puts it in the cell, and deposits her eggs on it. Like a bird, she sits on the eggs, protecting them from the chill of the early spring weather. The eggs hatch into worker bees who take over the building and enlarging of the nest. The worker bees are female bees unable to mate with males. The colony grows until there are a few hundred bees, but some colonies contain up to 2,000 bees. Toward the end of the summer, the queen lays eggs that hatch into males and queen bees. The new queen bees mate with the males. A few weeks later, all the bees die except the queen bees. They hibernate for the winter and start building new nests in the spring.

**Honeybees** Another social bee is the honeybee, which also belongs to the Apidae. This bee's body is dark brown with yellow bands. The honeybee is about 1.2 cm [0.5 in] long. Honeybees build their hives in tree hollows or in cracks in the walls of barns.

There is usually a lot of activity around the hives of honeybees. When the food supply is low, many bees must go out to gather a new supply. When food is plentiful, some of the bees remain behind the rest. They must continually inspect their hives to make sure everything is in order. They must be sure that it is kept in good repair. Bees returning with pollen and nectar let the other bees know where to find the food supply by doing special dancelike movements. The movements show how far away and in what direction from the hive the food can be found.

Domesticated honeybees, kept for production of honey, are called domestic bees. They are kept in wooden hives, which can be enlarged as the colony grows. Beekeepers remove honey from the hives during the summer, being careful to leave enough so that the bees can survive the winter.

A bee is an advanced insect that has complete metamorphosis. The first stage after the egg is a larva, or grub. During the second stage, many changes take place, preparing the way for the adult form. All this happens in the honeycomb.

**Social classes among honeybees**  The honeybee society has three main divisions: the workers, who provide food and protection for the colony; the queen, who lays the eggs; and the drones, who mate with the queen. An average honeybee hive contains 1 queen, 100 drones, and 60,000 workers.

The workers are female bees. They are the smallest bees in the hive. They can lay eggs but cannot mate, so the eggs are never fertilized. Each worker has a barbed stinger at the back end of the abdomen. When a bee stings another insect, it can withdraw its stinger without harm to itself. However, when a bee stings a large animal, the barbs on the stinger stick under the animal's skin. A part of the bee's abdomen is pulled off when the bee tries to withdraw its stinger. That is why a bee dies after it has stung a human.

For the first two weeks of a worker's adult life, she acts as a nurse. She feeds the queen, the drones, and the larvae. From the sixth day to the fourteenth day of her life, she secretes a substance called royal jelly from her mouth. When she is fourteen days old, she begins to produce wax from glands on the underside of her abdomen. She uses this wax to build the cells of the honeycomb. When a worker is three weeks old, she joins in the search for pollen and nectar. She also cleans the hive and stands guard at the hive's entrance.

Worker bees collect pollen from flowers and carry it in their sacs, or leg baskets. These sacs are rows of small spines on their rear legs. A single bee can collect balls of pollen as large as 6.3 mm [0.25 in] in diameter. The pollen is mixed with the bees' saliva to make beebread for food.

Nectar is also collected by the workers. They carry it in a special stomach called the crop or honey sac. A bee must visit about 1,000 flowers to fill its honey sac. It takes 60 full honey sacs to provide enough honey to fill a thimble. Honey is deposited in the honeycomb to ripen and thicken before the cell of the comb is sealed.

Workers use propolis, a resin from trees, to block up holes in their hives. They also use it to seal off the bodies of small animals who get into the hive and are stung to death.

Water is collected by the workers to dilute honey which has become too thick. It is also used to keep the hive moist and cool in hot weather.

Workers that are hatched in the spring or summer live from four to six weeks. Those that hatch in the fall live until the following spring.

The queen bee is nearly twice as large as the other bees. She usually lives from four to five years. Her function is to produce eggs so that the colony can continue. She may lay up to 3,000 eggs in one day. When a queen dies, the workers prepare queen cells for the last eggs that were laid. These cells are larger than other cells, and oblong rather than six-sided. Sometimes they are made while a queen is still alive. Eggs are placed in the queen cells and they hatch into larvae. The larvae are fed royal jelly for a longer period than the usual three days. This makes them develop into queen bees rather than into worker bees. When a queen comes out of her cell, she immediately seeks out and kills any other queen larvae in the hive. Should there be another adult queen present, the two will fight until one of them kills the other. A queen bee never stings any bee except another queen. If she is prevented from killing a rival queen, one or the other of them will leave the hive. She takes 2,000 to 20,000 bees along with her to start a new colony.

Drones are male bees born from unfertilized eggs laid by female workers. (*See* PARTHENOGENESIS.) Drones are larger than workers, but smaller than queens. Drones do not have stingers. Their tongues are not long enough for them to obtain nectar. That is why they must be fed by the workers.

The main function of the drones is to mate with the queen so that she can lay fertilized eggs. The mating begins when the queen and the drone fly out of the hive and mate in the air.

During the summer, about 100 drones are permitted to live in the hive and to be fed. If other drones appear, they are killed. When food becomes scarce in the fall, the drones in the colony are stung to death and removed from the hive.          S.R.G./J.R.

**BEECH FAMILY** The beech (bēch) family has about 400 species of trees, including the chestnut and oak. These trees grow to a height of 36.5 m (120 ft) in temperate and tropical regions. Beeches are monoecious, which means that both male and female flowers grow in the leaf axils of young shoots. The rounded male flowers are on thin stalks. The female flowers grow in pairs or in groups of three.

Beeches are deciduous, shedding their thin leaves once every year. The leaves are sometimes colored red or purple. The fruit of these trees, called mast, is an important food for animals. Beechwood is used for furniture, flooring, fuel, and as pulp in making paper.          J.J.A./M.H.S.

Beech leaf and nut.

The largest creature of its kind, the Goliath beetle measures up to eight inches [20 cm] in width. The smallest beetles cannot be seen without a microscope.

**BEETLE** (bēt' əl) Beetles are insects belonging to the order Coleoptera. There are at least 278,000 kinds of beetles. Four of every ten insects are beetles.

Beetles are most easily identified by their

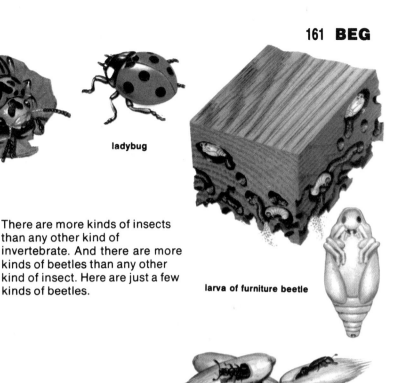

colorado beetle,
a pest of potatoes

ladybug

There are more kinds of insects than any other kind of invertebrate. And there are more kinds of beetles than any other kind of insect. Here are just a few kinds of beetles.

larva of furniture beetle

water beetle

weevils

elytra, a pair of hard shields that often cover the wings and most of the body. Beetles, which have strong jaws for biting, feed on plants and animals.

All insects have three-part bodies, made up of the head, the thorax, and the abdomen. But, unlike the bodies of other insects, the sections of the bodies of beetles are closely and strongly joined. Beetles are of many different colors. Some are brightly colored. Others are dull. Beetles develop from eggs to larvae to pupae to adults. (*See* METAMORPHOSIS.) Most live for one year. A few live for up to five years. Some may live for only a few weeks. Beetles may live in water, or above or under the ground. Some beetles are carnivores. Others are harmful to plant life. Beetles like the ladybug are helpful to plant life. They eat smaller insects, like aphids, that are harmful to plants.

Some beetles are too small to be seen with the naked eye. The largest beetle is the African Goliath beetle, which is the largest insect. Goliath beetles can grow to be 10 cm [4 in] long and 20 cm [8 in] wide.

The June beetle is common in the United States. It is a large, brown insect that can be seen on plants in the spring. The Japanese beetle is also common in the United States. It was brought from Asia to North America in 1916. Like the June beetle, it is a plant-eating pest. G.M.B./J.R.

**BEGONIA** (bi gōn′ yə) The begonia is a popular house plant with waxy leaves and brightly colored flowers. It grows mainly in tropical climates as a vine and shrub. The species cultivated in the United States is usually small. The blossoms may grow as single or double flowers, and their colors may be red, orange, yellow, white, or pink. Begonia leaves are smooth and shiny with a waxy covering.

The root of the begonia can be tuberous or fibrous. Those with tuberous roots have large flowers and bloom in the summer. The fibrous types are used as house plants and bloom in the winter. Many types, like the rex bogonia, have few flowers but are grown for their colorful leaves. P.G.C./M.H.S.

**BEHAVIOR OF ANIMALS** (bi hā′ vyər uv an′ ə məlz) Every species of animal acts differently. Each eats a certain food. Each lives in a certain place. Each reproduces in a certain way. The ways an animal acts are the behavior of the animal. The behavior of animals is defined as the way animals respond to their surroundings, or environment. Scientists who study animal behavior are called ethologists.

There are two main types of behavior: instinctive and learned. Instinctive behavior is behavior that the animal inherits from its parents. (*See* HEREDITY.) A young fish does not have to learn how to swim. It knows how to swim right after it is born. Learned behavior is behavior that has to be taught to the animal. A child does not know how to tie a shoe until he is taught to do so.

**Instinctive behavior** An ethologist can find out which behavior is learned by taking a very young animal away from all other members of its species. The animal's behavior will be instinctive because there is no other animal to teach it. If a bird that is hatched away from all other birds can fly, then flying is instinctive behavior. Most of the courtship and mating behavior by which an animal reproduces is instinctive. Instinctive behavior is caused, or triggered, by a signal called a releaser. Re-

leasers may be sights, sounds, smells, feels, or tastes. The sight of a hawk overhead is a releaser for a mouse to run and hide. The releaser for an animal to eat is hunger.

Many animals that live in groups have developed instinctive behavior which controls the group. (*See* ANT; BEE; EVOLUTION.) Examples of such social animals are insect colonies, schools of fish, herds of deer, and flocks of birds. Many birds flock together by instinct. Aggressive or unfriendly behavior is common among animals. But there is rarely an actual fight among members of the same species. It is even more rare for the animals to hurt or kill each other. Wolves may growl at each other. But before a fight actually begins, the younger or smaller wolf backs away. This instinctive behavior prevents animals from killing or harming members of their own group.

**Learned behavior** This kind of behavior is learned from experience. A dog learns to avoid a busy highway. If a cat learns that mice live in a woodpile, the cat will visit the area often. Many animals are trained by humans. Elephants dancing in a circus and dogs fetching a stick are displaying learned behavior. There are many different kinds of learned behavior. One of the most interesting kinds was discovered by Konrad Lorenz, an Aus-

Left, stags fight for dominance but rarely harm each other. Right, crowned cranes do a courtship dance.

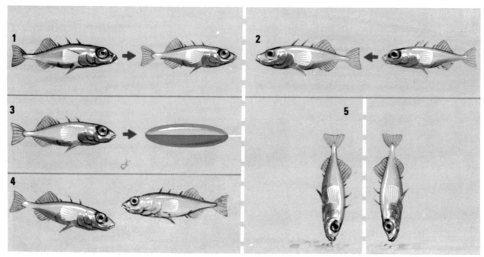

stickleback behavior

(1) The male stickleback chases other males out of his territory. (2) If the other male is chased into his own territory, he will turn, attack, and drive off the first stickleback. (3) A stickleback in his territory will attack even a dummy of the correct size and color. (4) He will pay no attention to a male stickleback that has been painted to conceal his red belly. (5) At the boundaries of their territories, sticklebacks display a peculiar kind of activity. They swim head downwards and pick up small stones in their mouths. This is an example of displacement activity, which may be connected with nest building.

trian ethologist. He learned that when a baby bird hatches from the egg, it identifies the first object it sees as its mother. He called this imprinting. When Lorenz artificially hatched goose eggs and stood next to the hatching eggs, the baby geese thought he was their mother. They followed him wherever he went.

Vertebrates have better developed brains than invertebrates, so they are better able to learn behavior. Mammals generally learn faster than other kinds of vertebrates, and humans learn behavior faster than any other species. *See also* ZOOLOGY.

S.R.G./R.J.B.

## BÉKÉSY, GEORG VON (1899–1972)
Georg von Békésy (bā′ kā′ shi) was a physicist and physiologist who is best known for his work on the way the ear receives sound. In 1961, he was awarded the Nobel Prize for physiology. He studied sound and the way it is analyzed and communicated to the brain by a part of the inner ear called the cochlea. Békésy experimented with the ears of dead people and animals, including an elephant. He constructed physical models that showed how sounds travel in the cochlea and along the basilar membrane of the ear. He worked at Harvard University and at the University of Hawaii. Summaries of his work can be found in his two books, *Experiments in Hearing* and *Sensory Inhibition. See also* EAR.

P.G.C./D.G.F.

## BELEMNITE (bel′ əm nīt′) A belemnite is a common fossil found in ancient rocks. It is shaped like a cigar with a point at one end. These fossils are the remains of the skeletons of extinct cephalopods related to the ammonites and present day cuttlefish. Belemnites are sometimes called the devil's thunderbolts because of their shape and appearance. *See also* AMMONITE; CEPHALOPOD.

C.M./A.I.

## BELL, ALEXANDER GRAHAM (1847–1922) Alexander Graham Bell (bel) was a Scottish-American scientist who invented the telephone. Born in Scotland, Bell and his family moved to Ontario, Canada, for health reasons. Bell's two brothers had died of tuberculosis, and Bell himself was showing

signs of the disease. Bell recovered within a year. At 23 years of age, Bell devoted himself to improving communication among the deaf.

While experimenting with the possibility of sending several telegraph signals over one wire at the same time, Bell became interested in sending voice sounds over a wire. In 1874, Bell secured the help of Thomas Augustus Watson, an expert in the field of telegraphy. (*See* TELEGRAPH.) Watson was of great help in Bell's early experiments. Bell was issued a patent for the telephone in 1876. A year later, he founded the Bell Telephone Company.

In his later years, Bell continued working on new inventions. Some of his ideas led to the development of the iron lung, the radio, phonograph records, the hydrofoil, and the metal detector. His chief interest, though, remained the education of the deaf. He used much of his money and influence to establish research and care institutions in Europe and the United States.      A.J.C./D.G.F.

Alexander Graham Bell, the Scottish teacher of the deaf whose invention of the telephone brought instant communication to everyone. Bell also experimented with simple flying machines and a device for transmitting speech on a beam of light—the first radio.

**BENDS** *See* CAISSON DISEASE.

**BENTHOS** (ben′ thäs′) Benthos is the name for all organisms that live on or in the bottom of a body of water. Benthic organisms live on top of the sand beneath the ocean, under the mud beneath a lake, or among the rocks of a streambed. They can be plants, insects, worms, crustaceans, fishes, or other kinds of organisms. Many of the benthic animals eat dead matter that falls to the bottom from the water above. Benthic organisms are also a valuable source of food for other aquatic animals.      S.R.G./R.J.B.

Benthos means "living at the bottom of the sea." These sea anemones are classified as benthic animals, even though they live in fairly shallow water.

**BENZ, KARL (1844–1929)** Born in Karlsruhe, Germany, Karl Benz (bents) was one of the first engineers to build motor-driven vehicles. He founded Benz and Company, in Mannheim, to manufacture gasoline engines. Benz started to build his first gas engine in 1879, building a practical automobile by 1885. He installed the gas engine on the back of a tricycle. The vehicle had an electric ignition, a water-cooled engine, shaped "poppet" valves, and a differential gear, features still common in automobiles today. A few months after Benz had finished his automobile, fellow German Gottlieb Daimler completed a motorcycle powered by a gasoline engine. Karl Benz later designed a float-type carburetor and a transmission system.      J.J.A./D.G.F.

**BENZENE** (ben′ zēn′) Benzene is a colorless liquid with a strong odor. It was discovered by Michael Faraday in 1825. Benzene, belonging to a group of compounds called aromatic hydrocarbons, gives off a vapor which is poisonous if breathed too long. The chemical formula for benzene is $C_6H_6$. It melts at 5.5°C [42°F] and boils at 80.1°C [176.2°F]. Benzene is sometimes called benzol. It should not be confused with benzine, a petroleum product of a different chemical makeup.

Benzene is produced by heating coal tar and condensing (changing to a liquid) the vapors from the tar. Large amounts of benzene are also obtained from petroleum. The benzene molecule has its carbon atoms arranged in a ring called a benzene ring. (See diagram.)

Benzene is used to dissolve resins and fats and to make chemical compounds. Benzene is used in various industries in the production of polystyrene, Styrofoam, synthetic rubber, nylon, synthetic detergents, and aniline dyes. *See also* HYDROCARBONS.

J.J.A./J.M.

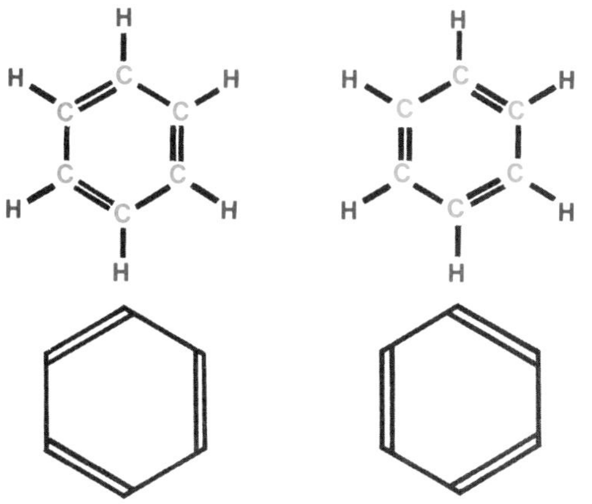

The molecule of benzene has six carbon atoms and six hydrogen atoms joined in a ring by alternate single and double bonds. These bonds may be shown, as here, in either of two arrangements. Benzene rings usually are drawn without the C and H symbols, as shown above.

**BERIBERI** (ber′ ē ber′ ē) Beriberi is a disease which affects the nervous system. It is caused by a lack of thiamine (vitamin B$_1$) in the diet. Beriberi causes severe pain and weakness in the arms and legs. It may also cause swelling of the body tissues or edema. In advanced cases, heart failure and death can occur.

Beriberi was very common in China, Japan, and the Philippines through the 19th century. The people in these countries had a diet consisting largely of polished white rice. It was found that polishing the rice removes thiamine. People who drink large amounts of alcohol usually have unbalanced diets and may suffer from beriberi. The disease can be treated with a diet of thiamine-rich foods such as unpolished cereal grains, green peas, and liver. Injections of synthetic thiamine are also effective. *See also* DIET; VITAMIN.

A.J.C./J.J.F.

**BERKELIUM** (bər′ klē əm) Berkelium (Bk) is a radioactive metallic element. It has an atomic number of 97. Its melting and boiling points have not yet been measured. Its relative density is about 14. Berkelium is not found in nature and has to be made artificially. It was made in 1949 by a team of American scientists led by Glenn T. Seaborg. They made it by bombarding the element americium with alpha particles. Eight isotopes of berkelium have been found so far. The m st stable isotope is berkelium-247. It takes 7,000 years for half of it to decay. Only very small amounts of the metal have been made so far. Because of this, no uses have yet been found for berkelium or its compounds. *See also* RADIOACTIVITY; TRANSURANIC ELEMENT.

M.E./J.R.W.

**BERNOULLI FAMILY** Bernoulli (ber nül′ ē) was the family name of three Swiss mathematicians and physicists. There were two brothers, Jacques and Jean, and Jean's son, Daniel. Born in Basel, each served as professor at the University of Basel.

Jacques Bernoulli (1654–1705) made important discoveries in mathematics. He worked on finite series and their sums, on calculus, and on trigonometry. He developed new material in the theory of probability. The Bernoulli numbers used in this branch of mathematics are named after him.

Jean Bernoulli (1667–1748) was also a mathematician, working on calculus and complex numbers. He worked in applied mathematics with subjects such as astronomy, the tides, optics, and ships' sails.

Daniel Bernoulli (1700–1782) was the best-known member of the family. He developed the science of hydrodynamics and one of his discoveries is known as Bernoulli's effect. It provides a means whereby the flow of fluids can be calculated. He also worked on differential equations, trigonometry, calculus, and probability theory. *See also* BERNOULLI'S EFFECT, CALCULUS, TRIGONOMETRY. J.J.A./D.G.F.

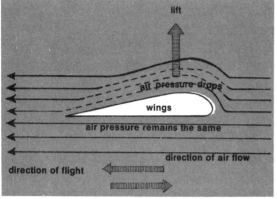

Bernoulli's effect is an important phenomenon in aerodynamics. Air flowing over the curved wing of a plane must arrive at the back edge at the same time as air flowing under the wing. So the air above flows faster.

**BERNOULLI'S EFFECT** (bər nü' lēz i fekt') As the speed of a fluid or gas increases, its pressure decreases. This is known as Bernoulli's effect. It was first described by Daniel Bernoulli in the 1700s. (*See* BERNOULLI FAMILY.) Although Bernoulli was referring to liquids flowing steadily at one level, the effect has many other applications.

Bernoulli's effect allows airplanes to fly. An airplane wing, seen from the tip, is flat on the bottom and curved on the top. As the wing travels through the air, the air must travel either over or under the wing. Air moving over the wing goes a longer distance so it must travel faster. Because air moving over the wing is moving faster, there is less air pressure on the top of the wing. This means that there is more pressure on the bottom of the wing, which pushes the wing upward, causing the plane to stay up in the air.

The same effect can be seen in a bathroom shower. Water from the shower moves the air inside the shower faster than the air outside the shower. This means there is more air pressure on the outside of the shower curtain than on the inside. As a result, the shower curtain blows inward. *See also* CONSERVATION OF ENERGY. A.J.C./J.T.

**BERRY** (ber' ē) In botany, the word berry refers to a small, simple fruit, or seeds in a fleshy substance enclosed by a skin. Common types of berries are the grape, tomato, citrus fruit, and melon. *See also* DRUPE.

P.G.C./F.W.S.

**EXAMPLES OF BERRIES**

holly berries

tomato

cucumber

lemon

melon

grapes

Berries have supplied food for people for many centuries. Animals in the wild rely on a wide variety of berries in their environment.

**BERYL** (ber' əl) Beryl is a hard mineral found mainly in granite rocks. In these rocks, beryl usually appears in the form of six-sided crystals, ranging in diameter from .64 cm [.25 in] to 30 cm [12 in]. Some beryl crystals have been found in Maine measuring about 5 m [18 ft] in length. Beryl is the common mineral of the rare element beryllium. In some areas, it is mined as beryllium ore. Important deposits are located in Brazil, India, South Africa, and in parts of the United States.

Most often yellowish green in color, beryls may also be red, green, blue, or yellow. Types of beryl include the dark green emerald, the blue green aquamarine, the rose morganite, and yellow golden beryl. For centuries, beryl has been used in the making of jewelry. J.J.A./R.H.

Six-sided crystals of beryl, the gemstone from which the metallic element beryllium is obtained. Some beryl crystals that weigh many tons have been found in nature.

**BERYLLIUM** (bə ril′ ē əm) Beryllium (Be) is a grayish white metallic element. Its atomic number is 4. Its atomic weight is 9.012. Beryllium melts at 1,280°C [2,336°F] and boils at 2,970°C [5,378°F]. Its relative density is 1.8. Beryllium is one of the alkaline earth metals. It was once known as glucinum. It was discovered in 1828 by Friedrich Wohler in Germany. A. A. Bussy discovered it in France in the same year. Beryllium is found in many minerals. Its most important source is the mineral beryl. Beryl is mined in Brazil, Argentina, and parts of the United States. Beryllium and its compounds are poisonous.

Beryllium is one of the lightest metals known and it can absorb a lot of heat. These two properties make beryllium useful in building rockets and spacecraft. It is also used to make strong alloys with copper, iron, aluminum, and other metals. M.E./J.R.W.

**BERZELIUS, JÖNS JAKOB (1779–1848)** Jöns Berzelius (bər ze′ liəs) was a Swedish chemist who was the first person to make a fairly accurate list of the atomic weights. He also developed the chemical symbols and formulas in use today. He studied the effects of electricity on solutions, introducing the idea of radicals.

Berzelius discovered the elements selenium, thorium, and silicon. Many of the terms used in chemistry, such as catalyst, isomer, and protein, were first used by Berzelius. Because of his many accomplishments, Jöns Berzelius was the most famous chemist of his time. J.J.A./D.G.F.

**BESSEMER, SIR HENRY (1813–1898)** Sir Henry Bessemer (bes′ ə mer) was an English inventor who developed an inexpensive process for making steel. The Bessemer process, introduced in 1856, blasts air through molten pig iron to burn out the impurities. This method greatly reduced the cost of producing steel. It has since been modified by using pure oxygen instead of air.

Bessemer was a self-educated engineer. In addition to his work with steel, he developed a solar furnace, a large telescope, and a type of gold powder used to tint paint. A.J.C./D.G.F.

**BETA PARTICLE** (bāt′ ə pärt′ i kəl) A beta particle is an electron (with a negative charge) or positron (with a positive charge). Beta particles are sent out in streams by the nuclei of certain radioactive atoms. The streams of beta particles are often called beta rays. These rays travel at a speed almost equal to that of light. Having such high energy, beta rays can pass through solid matter several millimeters thick. They ionize the substances through which they pass. Beta particles can be detected by Geiger counters and by photographic film. The other kinds of radiation produced by radioactive substances are alpha rays and gamma rays. *See also* ALPHA PARTICLE; RADIOACTIVE SERIES; RADIO-ACTIVITY. J.J.A./J.T.

**BETELGEUSE** (bēt′ əl jüz′) Betelgeuse is the ninth brightest star in the sky. It is part of Orion, the brightest constellation in the northern sky. Because of its color and size, Betelgeuse is classified as a red supergiant. It is red because of its temperature, which is much lower than that of yellow stars, like the sun. Stars with the highest temperatures are blue. Betelgeuse is about 400 times larger than the sun and between 450 and 550 light-years away from the earth. It is most visible in the northern hemisphere during December, when the constellation of Orion dominates the sky. The constellation seems to form the outline of the mythical hunter Orion. Betelgeuse is located at the right shoulder of the giant hunter. Its name comes from Arabic words meaning ''shoulder of the giant.'' G.M.B./C.R.

**BICEPS** (bī′ seps′) The biceps are muscles found in the human body. One biceps is attached to the front side of the arm. Its action has the effect of bending the forearm and helping in the rotation of the hand. It is called the biceps brachii. Another muscle, the biceps femoris, is found at the back of the thigh in the leg. It allows the lower leg to bend at the knee. P.G.C./J.J.F.

**BIENNIAL PLANT** Biennial (bī en′ ē əl) plants live for only two years. In the first year, they grow strong roots and leaves. Food is stored in the roots for use during the second year. As winter approaches biennial plants enter a time of dormancy during which very little growth takes place.

In the second year, biennial plants use the stored food to produce flowers and seeds. Some biennial plants are carrots, beets, and cabbage. These vegetables are eaten after the first season before the plant can flower. A.J.C./M.H.S.

**BIG DIPPER AND LITTLE DIPPER** The most familiar constellations in the northern hemisphere are the Big Dipper (big dip′ ər) and the Little Dipper (lit′ əl dip′ ər). The Big Dipper and the Little Dipper each have seven stars. Four stars make up the corners of the cup shapes. Three stars make up the handles.

Both of these constellations revolve around the North Star. The North Star is almost directly over the North Pole and forms the tip of the handle of the Little Dipper. It can be found most easily by following an imaginary line from the stars at the end of the cup of the Big Dipper.

The Big Dipper is part of the Ursa Major, or Great Bear, constellation. The Little Dipper is part of the Ursa Minor, or Little Bear, constellation. *See also* CELESTIAL SPHERE. A.J.C./C.R.

**BILHARZIA** (bil här′ zē ə) Bilharzia is a disease that is also known as schistosomiasis. It is found only in warm climates. The people of China and Egypt are often victims of the disease.

Bilharzia is caused by a parasitic worm. (*See* PARASITE.) The larva of the worm attaches itself to the skin of a swimmer and burrows into his flesh. Inside the person's body, the larva develops into an adult worm and feeds off of the person's blood. The worm tunnels through the inside of the body and causes serious injury. Bilharzia is difficult to treat and is often fatal. Scientists hope to control it by killing the worm larvae in the water. S.R.G./J.J.F.

**BIMETALLIC STRIP** (bī′ mə tal′ ik strip′) A bimetallic strip is made by fastening together two strips of different metals. The metals are often brass and iron. When different metals are heated, they expand by different amounts. This happens when a bimetallic strip is heated, and this causes the strip to bend. When it is cooled, the strip returns to its original shape. Bimetallic strips are used in some thermostats for controlling heating systems. When the temperature rises, the strip starts to bend. Eventually it bends so much that it stops the supply of gas or electricity to the heater. When the temperature drops, the strip bends back again and the supply is reconnected. *See also* EXPANSION.          M.E./J.T.

# BINARY NUMBERS

Binary numbers (bī′ nə rē nəm′ bərz) make up a number system that has 2 as its base. Every number system has a base, or quantity used as the starting point for calculation. The base of a number system can be any number at all. Throughout history, different number systems have been used by different cultures. The Babylonians based their system based on 60, The Romans on 12. The decimal system, based on 10, is used throughout the world now. With the advent of computers, the binary system, based on the number 2, has come into widespread use.

The kinds of numerals used in a number system depend on the base of the system. Ten symbols (0,1,2,3,4,5,6,7,8,9) must be used for the decimal sytem, which has a base of 10. In the binary system, only two symbols (0 and 1) are used. In any number system, quantities are shown by powers of the base. The notation (the way quantities are expressed in numbers) depends on the base of the system. In all systems, quantities are written as a row of numbers. Each position in the row means

something different. In the base 10 system, the positions are set up in columns in this way:

thousands ($10^3$) hundreds ($10^2$) tens ($10^1$) units ($10^0$)

5  2  3  6

Each column in the notation is like a kind of code:

The units column = $10^0$ = 1. (Any number to the power of 0 equals 1.)

The tens column = $10^1$ = 10. (Any number to the power of 1 equals itself.)

The hundreds column = $10^2$ = 100. (Any number to the power of 2 equals that number multiplied by itself.)

The thousands column = $10^3$ = 1000. (Any number to the power of 3 equals that number multiplied by itself twice.)

The numeral in each column shows how many of the numbers there are:

$$6 \times 10^0 = 6$$
$$3 \times 10^1 = 30$$
$$2 \times 10^2 = 200$$
$$5 \times 10^3 = 5000$$
Adding . . . 5,236

The same system is used for binary numbers, except that the base is 2, meaning that only 2 numerals, 1 and 0, need to be used. The numbers in parentheses show the position of the numeral, starting at the right:

(1) $2^0 = 1$　　(6) $2^5 = 32$
(2) $2^1 = 2$　　(7) $2^6 = 64$
(3) $2^2 = 4$　　(8) $2^7 = 128$
(4) $2^3 = 8$　　(9) $2^8 = 256$
(5) $2^4 = 16$　　(10) $2^9 = 512$
(11) $2^{10} = 1,024$
(12) $2^{11} = 2,048$
(13) $2^{12} = 4,096$
(14) $2^{13} = 8,192$

and so on.

| | | | |
|---|---|---|---|
| 1st column | $= 0 \times 2^0$ | $= 0$ | $= \_\ \_\ \_\ \_\ \_\ \_\ \_\ \_\ \_\ \_\ \_\ \_\ 0$ |
| 2nd column | $= 0 \times 2^1$ | $= 0$ | $= \_\ \_\ \_\ \_\ \_\ \_\ \_\ \_\ \_\ \_\ \_\ 0\ 0$ |
| 3rd column | $= 1 \times 2^2$ | $= 4$ | $= \_\ \_\ \_\ \_\ \_\ \_\ \_\ \_\ \_\ \_\ 1\ 0\ 0$ |
| 4th column | $= 0 \times 2^3$ | $= 0$ | $= \_\ \_\ \_\ \_\ \_\ \_\ \_\ \_\ \_\ 0\ 1\ 0\ 0$ |
| 5th column | $= 1 \times 2^4$ | $= 16$ | $= \_\ \_\ \_\ \_\ \_\ \_\ \_\ \_\ 1\ 0\ 1\ 0\ 0$ |
| 6th column | $= 1 \times 2^5$ | $= 32$ | $= \_\ \_\ \_\ \_\ \_\ \_\ \_\ 1\ 1\ 0\ 1\ 0\ 0$ |
| 7th column | $= 1 \times 2^6$ | $= 64$ | $= \_\ \_\ \_\ \_\ \_\ \_\ 1\ 1\ 1\ 0\ 1\ 0\ 0$ |
| 8th column | $= 0 \times 2^7$ | $= 0$ | $= \_\ \_\ \_\ \_\ \_\ 0\ 1\ 1\ 1\ 0\ 1\ 0\ 0$ |
| 9th column | $= 0 \times 2^8$ | $= 0$ | $= \_\ \_\ \_\ \_\ 0\ 0\ 1\ 1\ 1\ 0\ 1\ 0\ 0$ |
| 10th column | $= 0 \times 2^9$ | $= 0$ | $= \_\ \_\ \_\ 0\ 0\ 0\ 1\ 1\ 1\ 0\ 1\ 0\ 0$ |
| 11th column | $= 1 \times 2^{10}$ | $= 1024$ | $= \_\ \_\ 1\ 0\ 0\ 0\ 1\ 1\ 1\ 0\ 1\ 0\ 0$ |
| 12th column | $= 0 \times 2^{11}$ | $= 0$ | $= \_\ 0\ 1\ 0\ 0\ 0\ 1\ 1\ 1\ 0\ 1\ 0\ 0$ |
| 13th column | $= 1 \times 2^{12}$ | $= 4096$ | $= 1\ 0\ 1\ 0\ 0\ 0\ 1\ 1\ 1\ 0\ 1\ 0\ 0$ |
| Adding . . . | | $\overline{5{,}236}$ | $= 1010001111110$ |

In binary notation, there is either a 0 or a 1 in each column. A 0 in a column means that the quantity in that column equals 0 multiplied by the base (2) to the power of that column. Since 0 multiplied by anything equals 0, a 0 in a column equals a quantity of 0. A 1 in a column means that the quantity in that column equals 1 multiplied by the base (2) to the power of that column. In binary notation, it would take 13 columns to show the quantity 5,236.

Binary arithmetic is simple. For addition, only the rules $0 + 0 = 0$, $0 + 1 = 1$, $1 + 0 = 1$, and $1 + 1 = 10$ ($1 \times 2^1$ and $0 \times 2^0$) need to be known. Multiplication can be performed using the rules $0 \times 0 = 0$, $0 \times 1 = 0$, $1 \times 0 = 0$, and $1 \times 1 = 1$. The following shows two examples using binary numbers:

```
     1100           1100
   +  101         ×  101
   ------         ------
    10001           1100
                   1100
                  ------
                  111100

 12 + 5 = 17     12 × 5 = 60
```

Subtraction and division are also easy to perform. When it is necessary to borrow in subtraction, remember that binary 10 (decimal 2) is borrowed, not decimal 10 as in ordinary arithmetic.

```
   10001             1100
 -   101        101)111100
 -------            101
    1100            ---
                    101
 17 − 5 = 12        101
                    ---
                    000
                60 ÷ 5 = 12
```

Binary numbers are more helpful for use in computers than decimal numbers. Because there are only two numerals, 0 and 1, the numeral 1 can be coded by the computer as a single electrical pulse. The numeral zero can be coded as the lack of an electrical pulse.

J.J.A./S.P.A.

The bindweed family includes about 1,100 species. Most of these plants are climbers that are native to the warmer regions of the world. The convolvulus, shown here, with its white trumpet-shaped flowers, is a typical bindweed. The morning glory and the sweet potato also belong to this family.

**BINDWEED FAMILY** There are more than 1,100 species of plants in the bindweed (bīn″ dwēd′) family. They are all dicotyledons. Most are perennial, woody plants. These plants are weeds that climb and grow around other plants, often killing the other plants in the process. Members of the bindweed family are found throughout the United States and southern Canada, as well as in Europe and parts of Asia. They grow along roads, beaches, and fields.

Most bindweeds have arrow-shaped leaves and funnel-shaped flowers. Some familiar varieties are the morning glory and sweet potato. The hedge bindweed and field bindweed often grow among cultivated crops, causing extensive damage. Dodders and convolvulus are two annual herbaceous varieties of this parasitic plant. *See also* HERBACEOUS PLANT; PARASITE; RHIZOME.    A.J.C./M.H.S.

**BINET, ALFRED (1857–1911)** Alfred Binet (bē′ ne′) was a French psychologist who developed the first intelligence test for children. The French government asked Binet to design a test that could identify children who seemed to be less intelligent than the average. The learning ability of these children is usually much less than that of other children

the same age. The purpose of the tests was to allow educators to decide which children needed special schooling.

In 1905, working with Theodore Simon, Binet developed the Binet-Simon intelligence tests. These were the first scales for measuring intelligence, or discovering "mental age." They helped teachers to find out the relative intelligence of their students. Later, the tests were used to find a child's intelligence quotient (IQ). The IQ is a number equal to the mental age, as determined by testing, divided by the actual, or chronological age of the person tested, and then multiplied by 100. If a person's intelligence is average, then his mental age and his chronological age are the same. Divide one by the other and the answer is 1. Multiply 1 by 100 and the answer is, of course, 100. The IQ of an average person is 100.    J.J.A./D.G.F.

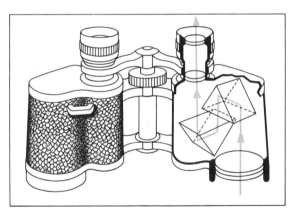

Binoculars are instruments designed for use with both eyes to get a close-up view of things at a distance. The best binoculars contain prisms. Each tube contains two prisms arranged as shown in this diagram. The arrows show how the light is bent four times as it passes through the instrument.

**BINOCULARS** (bə näk′ yə lərz) Binoculars are a pair of small telescopes built into a frame, or casing. They allow stereoscopic vision, which is the ability to judge depth by using both eyes at the same time. Binoculars make distant objects seem closer by means of magnification.

The two telescopes in binoculars are exactly alike. Each telescope is built into a funnel-shaped tube, or cylinder. An objective lens is at the wider end of each tube. An eyepiece, consisting of one or more lenses, is at the narrower end of each tube. Each tube contains two prisms located between the objective and eyepiece lenses.

The objective lenses gather light from the object being viewed. They form images that are upside down and reversed right-to-left. By bending the light beams, the prisms correct the image to proper orientation before it reaches the eyepiece lenses. The eyepiece lenses further magnify the image.

Most binoculars have adjusting wheels, or knobs, that change the distances between the objective lenses and the eyepiece lenses. This movement of the lenses closer or farther apart brings the object into focus. Some binoculars have one focus wheel for both telescope tubes. The better binoculars have controls for independent focus of each telescope.

Binoculars usually have two numbers printed or engraved somewhere on the outer covering. The first number is the power or magnification. The second number is the diameter of the objective lens in millimeters. Binoculars that are marked 6 × 35, for example, will magnify an object six times through an objective lens that is 35 mm [1.4 in] in diameter.

Many modern microscopes are arranged in binocular fashion. This makes looking into the microscope more comfortable and gives the viewer a three-dimensional image.

G.M.B./S.S.B.

**BIOCHEMISTRY** (bī′ ō kem′ ə strē) Biochemistry is the science that studies the chemical makeup and behavior of all living things. The whole structure of living things is built up from chemical substances. These substances are constantly changing. Complex molecules are being broken down into simpler parts. Simple parts are being built up again. Such changes take place under the control of substances called enzymes. Enzymes, working together, make up a creature's metabolism.

The study of biochemistry began late in the eighteenth century. Chemicals were taken from living things and studied. Antoine Lavoisier discovered the body's use of oxygen. Since late in the nineteenth century, biochemists have made many discoveries. Some important discoveries are connected with the use of food in building tissues and supplying energy. Biochemists have discovered how plants use energy from the sun to build simple substances into more complex ones by photosynthesis. They have found how animals break down foods by digestion into simpler parts, and then build these up again. Biochemists have also traced the complex series of reactions linked with the Krebs cycle. This cycle releases the energy in food molecules. Biochemists have studied special molecules in the cell called nucleic acids. Scientists believe these acids may be the controllers of all growth and reproduction. One form of nucleic acid, RNA, is found throughout the cell, where it controls the making of protein. DNA is another form of nucleic acid. DNA carries and passes a kind of "blueprint" or plan of a living thing from one generation to the next. Biochemistry is also concerned with the workings of membranes, with the chemical changes taking place in muscles as they contract, and in nerve cells as they conduct messages.

Through its discoveries of how the body functions in health and sickness, biochemistry has contributed to medicine. It has led to the understanding and treatment of metabolic diseases in which the body's chemistry goes wrong. Pharmacology, the study of drugs and their actions, is closely related to biochemistry. Techniques of biochemistry, such as chemical analysis, chromatography, and the use of radioisotopes as "tracers," are valuable in the study of many diseases. Biochemists are helping to learn some of the causes of mental illness, the origins of birth defects, and how poor diet affects intelligence.          J.J.A./E.R.L.

**BIOLOGICAL CONTROL** (bī′ ə läj′ i kəl kən trōl′) Biological control is a method of fighting pests by using their natural enemies against them. A well-known example is the use of a pet cat to catch mice in a house. The use of a mousetrap or poison to catch mice is not biological control because people made the trap and poison. Biological controls are often better than artificial controls. Poisons that are meant to kill a pest can often kill helpful species, too. When pesticides get into human food, such as corn or fish, humans who eat the food can become very sick. Biological controls do not have such harmful side effects.

Most species of plants and animals do not become serious pests because their natural enemies eat many of them. If the natural enemies suddenly disappear, the population of the species can grow so large that the species becomes a pest. This happened to the deer in New Jersey. All of the deer's enemies—wolves, bears, cougars—left the area because of the building of cities. Hunting was not allowed in a state park. The deer became so numerous that they were eating the trees in the woods, running in front of cars, and starving. When hunting was again allowed, the number of deer went down, and the problems went away.

Each region of the world has different animals. Sometimes animals are taken from one region to another by people. Because the animal has never lived in the new region before, it may not have any enemies there. It can become a pest. Starlings, carp, and gypsy moths are animals that became pests when they were brought to the United States. To control pests such as these, scientists find the pests' natural enemies and bring them to the new region, too. The scientists must be careful because the enemy can also become a pest.

An example of biological control is seen in this shield bug, which is feeding on the destructive larva of the noctuid moth.

A hoverfly larva feeds on aphids that are infesting a rose plant. This is a commonly encountered example of biological control in nature.

Cinnabar moth caterpillars are feeding on a ragwort plant, which is poisonous to cattle.

Scientists now know that it is best not to let foreign animals loose in a new land without carefully studying their effect on the environment.                          E.R.L./S.R.G.

**BIOLOGICAL RHYTHM** (bī′ ə läj′ i kəl rith′ əm) Cycles that occur regularly to living things are called biological rhythms. Sleeping is a biological rhythm in humans because they sleep every day. Some rhythms are behavior, like sleeping. Other rhythms are body functions, like a heartbeat.

Biological rhythms occur without the organism controlling them. For example, the human heart beats constantly, people sleep regularly, and their blood pressure changes regularly. Yet organisms do not control these functions on purpose. They happen by themselves.

No one knows exactly how biological rhythms work. Scientists say that organisms have a "built-in clock" that "tells" the organisms what time of day it is. For instance, certain species of mice are only active at night. When these mice are kept in a cage that is dark all day, they still sleep during the day and are active at night. Their "built-in clock" tells them when night has come, even though their eyes cannot tell.

There are several kinds of biological rhythms. Some happen twice a day. Crabs come out of their holes at every low tide. Some kinds of biological rhythms happen once a day, like humans sleeping. These daily rhythms are called circadian, which means 'about a day' in Latin. Other rhythms happen once a month, like the menstrual cycle in women. These cycles are called lunar, which refers to the moon. Annual rhythms happen once a year, like flowers blossoming on a plant in the spring.          S.R.G./E.R.L.